AQA GCSE (9–1)

Combined Science

Required Practicals Lab Book:
Exam practice and further application

David Johnston
Adrian Schmit
Matt Shooter

HODDER
EDUCATION
AN HACHETTE UK COMPANY

Every effort has been made to trace all copyright holders, but if any have been inadvertently overlooked, the Publishers will be pleased to make the necessary arrangements at the first opportunity.

Although every effort has been made to ensure that website addresses are correct at time of going to press, Hodder Education cannot be held responsible for the content of any website mentioned in this book. It is sometimes possible to find a relocated web page by typing in the address of the home page for a website in the URL window of your browser.

Hachette UK's policy is to use papers that are natural, renewable and recyclable products and made from wood grown in well-managed forests and other controlled sources. The logging and manufacturing processes are expected to conform to the environmental regulations of the country of origin.

Orders: please contact Bookpoint Ltd, 130 Park Drive, Milton Park, Abingdon, Oxon OX14 4SE. Telephone: +44 (0)1235 827827. Fax: +44 (0)1235 400401. Email education@bookpoint.co.uk Lines are open from 9 a.m. to 5 p.m., Monday to Saturday, with a 24-hour message answering service. You can also order through our website: www.hoddereducation.co.uk

ISBN: 978 1 5104 5150 6

© Adrian Schmit, David Johnston and Matt Shooter 2019

First published in 2019 by

Hodder Education,

An Hachette UK Company

Carmelite House

50 Victoria Embankment

London EC4Y 0DZ

www.hoddereducation.co.uk

Impression number   10   9   8   7   6   5   4   3   2   1

Year   2023   2022   2021   2020   2019

Cover photo © tulpahn - stock.adobe.com

Typeset in Helvetica Neue Light 8/9 by Aptara, Inc.

Printed in Great Britain by CPI Group.

A catalogue record for this title is available from the British Library.

MIX
Paper from
responsible sources
FSC™ C104740

Contents

Completed

PHYSICS

Answers can be found in the accompanying teacher book and also online at www.hoddereducation.co.uk/AQAGCSELabBook

How to use this book

This book will help you to keep a record of the required practicals you have completed, as well as your results and conclusions. It covers the following specifications:

- AQA GCSE (9–1) Combined Science: Trilogy
- AQA GCSE (9–1) Combined Science: Synergy.

To see how these two specifications match up against each other, see the chart below:

Matching chart

	AQA Combined Trilogy	AQA Synergy
BIOLOGY	Required Practical 1	3
	Required Practical 2	4
	Required Practical 3	7
	Required Practical 4	20
	Required Practical 5	10
	Required Practical 6	8
	Required Practical 7	12
CHEMISTRY	Required Practical 8	17
	Required Practical 9	21
	Required Practical 10	18
	Required Practical 11	19
	Required Practical 12	9
	Required Practical 13	11
PHYSICS	Required Practical 14	2
	Required Practical 15	16
	Required Practical 16	15
	Required Practical 17	1
	Required Practical 18	13
	Required Practical 19	14
	Required Practical 20	5
	Required Practical 21	6

Practical structure

Completing the practical

At the start of each practical, we have provided a brief context to help explain how the science behind the practical ties in to the wider course. There are also page references for further information, which will direct you to the following titles:

- **AQA GCSE (9–1) Combined Science Student Book**
- **AQA GCSE (9–1) Combined Science 1 Student Book**
- **AQA GCSE (9–1) Combined Science 2 Student Book**

The first page reference shown will always be to the **AQA GCSE (9–1) Combined Science Student Book**. If the pages ranges are different in the **Combined Science 1** and **Combined Science 2** books, they will be shown as: (or CS 2: 92–93). If this second reference is not given the page range is the same as in the all-in-one book.

The aim of each practical is then laid out, along with a list of **equipment** needed to complete the practical as suggested. Your teacher will inform you whether they have decided to change any of the equipment, and if the method needs to be adapted as a result.

Before you begin the practical and start on the **method** it is vital that you read and understand the **health and safety notes**, as well as taking any necessary precautions as stated. See the Health and safety feature below for more details. Once you have carried out a risk assessment and made everything safe, you should check with your teacher that it is appropriate to begin working through the method.

The **method** itself is presented in a step-by-step fashion and you should read it through at least once before starting, making sure you understand everything. Then, ensuring that you don't miss anything out, you should work through the practical safely. **Tips** may be provided to help with particularly problematic steps.

Observations and questions

Within each practical there is a clear section for **observations** where you should record your results as you complete the practical (although you may wish to do additional workings on separate paper). Scaffolded questions are also provided to help you develop **conclusions** and **evaluate** the success of the experiment.

Once the practical is completed, there are **exam-style questions** that relate to the practical and which provide useful practice. Your teacher may decide to set this as part of the lesson or at a later date. This is followed by a **further application** section, which provides additional questions that apply the scientific theory learned from the practical to different contexts. This will help you to consolidate your understanding.

Other features to help you through the practical include:

Health and safety

Each practical includes health and safety guidance to help you carry out the experiment safely. However, it is still the duty and legal obligation of schools to carry out their own risk assessments for each practical in accordance with local health and safety requirements.

Key terms

These are key terms and definitions that will help you understand vocabulary relevant to the practical. A full list of key terms is provided on **pages 148–149**.

Key equations

If a practical requires the use of a particular equation in either the results or the subsequent questions, these are usually flagged in this section. Some of the more commonly-known equations may have been omitted to mimic the actual exam papers. A full list of equations is provided on **pages 144–147**.

Maths opportunities

Opportunities to cover the recommended mathematic skills are flagged in these boxes. These will usually only list the mathematic skills most relevant to the practical, and additional minor skills may also be covered.

Tips

Guidance about, for example, the recommended way to complete a practical or answer certain questions.

Notes

These are used to highlight additional practical notes that needed flagging, for example if there is a particular recommended way to carry out a practical, or if there are multiple ways that a question can be answered to get the mark.

Answers to all questions are provided in the accompanying teacher book. They can also be found online here: **www.hoddereducation.co.uk/AQAGCSELabBook**.

The accompanying teacher book is available at **www.hoddereducation.co.uk/AQATeacherLabBook** and can also be bought as part of a classroom pack at **www.hoddereducation.co.uk/AQACombinedSciLabClassroomPack**.

How you will be assessed

Assessment information

In AQA GCSE (9–1) Science, you are not assessed on the required practicals independently. However, you are expected to complete these experiments as part of the wider science course in the exam.

In both Combined Science: Trilogy and Synergy, questions on these (or similar) practicals count for at least 15% of the overall marks. In the Synergy exams, the required practicals will be mostly tested in Paper 2 (Life and Environmental Sciences, Topics 4.1–4.4) and Paper 4 (Physical Science, Topics 4.5–4.8).

It is important to note that the exams are **not** restricted to asking questions on these specific practicals, and instead are designed to focus on investigative skills. This means they are likely to test how well you can apply your practical knowledge to unfamiliar contexts. It is for this reason that we have included the **further application** sections within this lab book.

You should be sure to keep this book safe as it may prove a useful resource when it comes to revising for your exams.

Required practical 1: Using a light microscope to observe animal and plant cells

In this practical you will use a light microscope to observe, draw and label examples of plant and animal cells, including a scale magnification. The specification does not require you to prepare your own slide in this practical, but this is an opportunity to practise the skill, which is often necessary in microscope work.

You will prepare microscope slides of onion epidermal cells and cheek cells, using appropriate stains to enable them to be viewed under a light microscope. You will then produce an accurate drawing of a selection of cells of each type, and calculate the magnification of your drawings.

Aim

Preparation and examination of slides of onion epidermis and cheek cells using a light microscope, drawing a selection of cells from each slide and calculating the magnification of the drawings.

Equipment and reagents

- Onion
- Knife or scalpel
- White tile
- Sterile cotton wool bud
- Forceps
- Microscope slide (×2)
- Coverslip (×2)
- Mounted needle
- Microscope
- Dropping pipette
- Iodine solution (0.01 mol/dm³) in a dropping bottle
- 1% methylene blue stain in a dropping bottle
- Filter paper

Key equations

total magnification = magnification of eyepiece lens × magnification of objective lens

$$\text{real size} = \frac{\text{image size}}{\text{magnification}}$$

Further information

Further information can be found in the **AQA GCSE (9–1) Combined Science Student Book** on pages:
- 2–3: Eukaryotes and prokaryotes
- 4–6: Animal and plant cells
- 7–8: Using a light microscope to observe plant and animal cells.

Health and safety

- Iodine solution can be an irritant to eyes. You should wear eye protection when handling iodine solution. You should also take care when using iodine solution to prevent staining of skin, clothes or equipment.
- Scalpels/knives can cut. Cut the onion on the tile, not in your hand. Always cut away from your fingers or thumb.
- Care needs to be taken when handling microscope slides and coverslips to prevent breakages and the risks associated with sharp, broken glass.

Maths opportunities

- Multiplication/division
- Making estimates to judge relative size

Method

Part A: Onion epidermis

1 Split and pull the onion apart into layers.
2 With the scalpel, make a square cut partway through an onion segment.
3 Using the forceps, carefully peel the inner epidermal cell layer away from the onion (see diagram below). The epidermal layer (or **epidermis**) is an outer 'skin' one cell thick on the inside and outside of each of the layers of the onion. Use the inner side of the onion layer for this procedure.

Key term

Epidermis: the outer layer of cells covering an organism.

Note

Make sure that your cut is on the side of the segment that was towards the inside of the onion, and that the square cut is smaller than the coverslip.

Epidermal layer   Forceps

Onion

4 Place a drop of water onto the centre of the slide.

5 Gently lay the sheet of epidermis onto the drop of water. Try to avoid trapping air bubbles underneath the tissue.

6 Put two drops of iodine solution onto the onion tissue.

7 Carefully lower a coverslip onto the slide. Place one edge of the coverslip on the slide and use a mounted needle to lower the other edge onto the slide. Soak up any liquid from around the edge of the coverslip using some filter paper.

8 Put the slide on the microscope stage.

9 Leave for a few minutes for the dye to stain the cells, then observe the slide under the microscope.

Part B: Cheek cells

1 Gently scrape the inside of your cheek with the cotton wool bud.

2 Smear the sample from the bud gently onto your microscope slide.

3 Add a drop or two of water to the part of the slide you smeared.

4 Place the coverslip onto the slide. Place one edge on the slide and then gently lower the coverslip down.

5 Add a drop of methylene blue dye near one edge of the coverslip, on the microscope slide.

6 Draw the dye under the coverslip by putting the filter paper next to the opposite edge of the coverslip to the dye.

7 Leave for a few minutes for the dye to stain the cells, then observe the slide under the microscope.

Part C: Observing and drawing

1 Select the lowest power objective lens (×40 magnification).

2 Without looking through the eyepiece, turn the coarse adjustment knob so that the end of the objective lens is almost touching the slide.

3 Looking through the eyepiece, turn the coarse adjustment knob to increase the distance between the objective lens and the slide until the cells come into focus.

4 Rotate the fine adjustment knob to bring the cells into a clear focus and use the low power objective to look at the cells.

5 When you have found some cells, switch to a higher power objective lens (×100 or ×400 magnification). Remember to look from the side, and not through the eyepiece itself, when you are adjusting the lens.

6 Make a clear, labelled drawing of four or five of the cells from each slide and their components.

7 Using the eyepiece **graticule**, measure the length of one of the epidermal cells that you have drawn (the microscope should be calibrated so you know the length of one eyepiece graticule division).

8 Now measure the length of the same cell in your drawing.

9 Calculate the magnification of your drawing.

10 Write the magnification underneath your drawing.

Tip

Cheek cells are much thinner than onion epidermis cells, and this can make them quite difficult to find. Remember that they can only be seen when the microscope is precisely focused.

Health and safety

- Avoid touching the end of the cotton bud with anything before putting it in your mouth.
- Methylene blue is harmful and an irritant. Make sure to wear eye protection.

Key term

Graticule: a glass disc with a measurement scale engraved on it, inserted into the eyepiece of a microscope.

Key equations

Use the following formula to calculate the magnification of your drawing:

$$\text{magnification} = \frac{\text{length of drawing of cell}}{\text{actual length of cell}}$$

Biology

Observations

1 In the boxes below, draw labelled diagrams of the cheek cells and the onion cells that you viewed under the microscope.

Cheek cells	Onion cells

2 Both animal and plant cells have nuclei. In the onion epidermis, the nucleus is not visible in all cells. Suggest a reason for this.

....

....

....

Conclusions

3 If you use a ×10 eyepiece lens and a ×20 objective lens, what will be the magnification of the image seen?

....

4 Name an organelle found in both plant and animal cells that is **not** visible in either cheek cells or onion epidermal cells seen under the light microscope.

....

Evaluation

5 Chloroplasts can be found in many plant cells. Suggest why onion epidermal cells do not have them.

....

....

....

6 Why would it be incorrect to give the magnification calculated in question 3 as the magnification of the drawing?

....

....

....

....

Exam-style questions

1   A student observed some onion epidermal cells under a light microscope. The image seen is shown below.

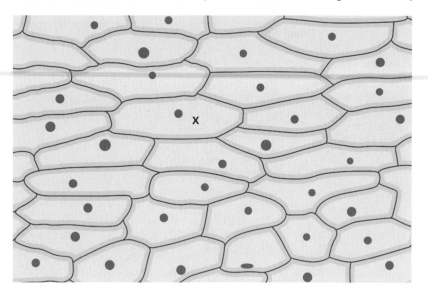

a) The magnification of the image is ×200. Calculate the length of cell X in mm. Show your working.   **[2]**

....

....

....

b) Name a structure visible in the image above that would not be seen in animal cells.   **[1]**

....

c) The cells in the diagram have been stained with iodine. Explain why they would not be seen without the use of a stain.   **[1]**

....

....

d) Name **two** structures found in plant cells (but not in animal cells) that are not visible in the image above.   **[2]**

....

....

2   Describe the procedure for making a microscope slide of onion epidermis to be viewed under a light microscope.   **[6]**

....

....

....

....

....

....

....

....

[Total = ... **/12 marks]**

Biology

Further application

1 a) Use the data provided about microscopic structures to fill in the gaps in the table below. [4]

Structure	Length on a microscope drawing	Magnification of microscope drawing	Real length of structure
A	20 mm	×100	
B		×60	0.5 mm
C	4 cm		0.8 mm
D	3 cm	×200	

b) A student uses a microscope with a ×10 eyepiece lens and a ×40 objective lens. What will be the magnification of the image seen through the microscope? [1]

....

c) Why is a coverslip used when preparing a microscope slide? [1]

....

d) Why is it important to lower the coverslip carefully and slowly when preparing a microscope slide? [1]

....

....

2 A student observed some cells from a potato that had been scraped onto a microscope slide. Starch grains could be seen as purplish dots. The only other structures that could be seen were nuclei, which were stained brown, and the cell walls, visible as a border around each cell.

a) What is the function of starch grains in a plant cell? [1]

....

b) From the information in the question, which stain had been used on these cells? Explain your answer. [2]

....

....

....

c) Name an organelle found in all plant cells that was not visible in these cells. [1]

....

d) In the winter, the potato plant dies, leaving just the potatoes underground. The following year, stems grow from structures called 'eyes' in the potato to become new potato plants. Suggest a role for the starch grains in this process. [3]

....

....

....

....

[Total = .../ 14 marks]

Required practical 2: Investigating the effect of sugar or salt on the mass of plant tissue

In this practical you will investigate the effect of a range of concentrations of sugar or salt solutions on the mass of plant tissue. Water moves by the process of **osmosis** from a solution of higher **water potential** (i.e. more dilute) to one of lower water potential (i.e. more concentrated). The movement of water can be traced by measuring mass changes in living tissue.

Aim

Investigate the effect of a range of concentrations of sugar (or salt) solutions on the mass of plant tissue.

Equipment and reagents

- Potato
- Cork borer
- Rule
- 10 cm³ measuring cylinder
- Labels
- Five boiling tubes
- Test tube rack
- Paper towels
- Scalpel
- White tile
- Range of sugar or sodium chloride solutions (0.25, 0.5, 0.75 and 1.0 mol/dm³)
- Distilled water
- Top-pan balance accurate to at least 0.01 g

Maths opportunities

- Subtraction
- Calculating percentages
- Recognise and use expressions in decimal form
- Calculating means
- Plotting variables, and translating information between graphical and numerical forms
- Understanding linear graphs

Method

1. Label four of the boiling tubes with the different concentrations of solution used, and label the fifth one 'water'.
2. Add 10 cm³ of the appropriate sugar/salt solution to the first four tubes, and add 10 cm³ of distilled water to the one labelled 'water'.
3. Use a cork borer to cut five potato cylinders of the same diameter.
4. Use a scalpel to cut the cylinders so that they are all 3 cm in length.
5. Use a balance to measure the mass of the first cylinder. Record the result in the 'Distilled water' column of the table in the **observations** section of the questions on page 7. Then place this cylinder in the 'water' tube.
6. Repeat step 5 with the other four potato cylinders, placing each one in a tube marked with the appropriate concentration. Ensure that you write the correct values in the correct columns of your table.
7. Leave the potato cylinders in the boiling tubes overnight.
8. Remove the cylinder from the 1 M sugar/salt tube and measure its mass. Record your results in your table (in the **observations** section).
9. Repeat step 8 for each of the other cylinders, ensuring that the results are recorded in the correct column.
10. Calculate the percentage change in mass for each.
11. Draw a graph of your results with 'Concentration of sugar/salt solution/M' on the *x*-axis and 'Percentage change in mass' on the *y*-axis.

Further information can be found in the **AQA GCSE (9–1) Combined Science Student Book** on pages:
- 29–32: Diffusion
- 33–35: Osmosis.

Key terms

Osmosis: the net movement of water molecules through a selectively permeable membrane from a more dilute solution to a more concentrated solution.

Water potential: a measure of the tendency of water to move from one area to another due to osmosis.

Health and safety

- Wear eye protection.
- Scalpels, knives and cork borers can cut. If you are cutting your own potato cylinders, care should be taken.

Key equation

$$\% \text{ change in mass} = \frac{\text{change in mass}}{\text{initial mass}} \times 100$$

Note

Controlling the length and diameter of the potato cylinders controls the surface area.

Note

As we are controlling the length and diameter, it is impossible to control the mass as well. We account for this by recording percentage change in mass.

Tip

It is best to blot the cylinders dry with paper tissue, so that any water on the surface is not weighed.

Observations

1 Record your results in the following table:

	Distilled water	0.25 mol/dm³ solution	0.5 mol/dm³ solution	0.75 mol/dm³ solution	1.0 mol/dm³ solution
Initial length/mm					
Final length/mm					
Initial mass/g					
Final mass/g					
% change in mass					

2 Describe any trend seen in your results.

....

....

....

Conclusions

3 When the concentration of the outside solution is the same as that of the **cell sap** in the potato cells, the mass of the potato cylinder will not change. Explain why.

....

....

....

Key term

Cell sap: The solution found in the central vacuole of plant cells. Sugars are the principal solutes.

4 Use your graph to estimate the concentration of the cell sap in the potato cells.

....

....

Evaluation

5 To make the test fair, it was important that the cylinders were all the same length. Explain why.

....

....

6 Why was percentage change in mass used to plot the graph, rather than just change in mass?

....

....

7 The practical could have used change in length of the cylinders as the dependent variable. Suggest why change in mass is likely to give more accurate results.

....

....

....

....

8 Suggest one way in which the strength of evidence could be improved in this experiment.

....

....

Exam-style questions

1 A student weighed five cylinders of potato, of equal length and diameter, then placed them into different strengths of sugar solution and left them for 24 hours. They then re-weighed them and recorded the percentage change in mass. Their results are shown below.

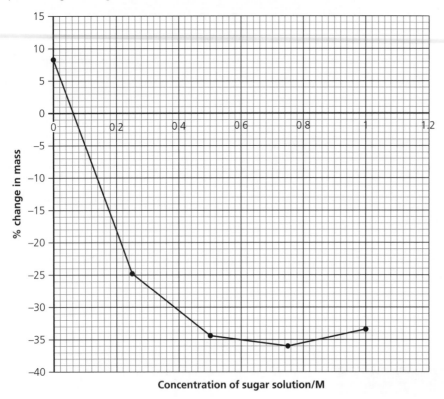

Concentration of sugar solution/M

a) Name the process that is causing the change in mass.   [1]

....

b) Describe the trend seen in the results.   [3]

....

....

....

c) Explain the percentage change in mass seen in distilled water (0 M).   [3]

....

....

....

....

d) Explain the results between 0.5 and 1.0 M.   [3]

....

....

....

Biology

2   Some students prepared three cylinders of potato of equal diameter and length. They placed each cylinder into water baths at three different temperatures and left them for 30 minutes. The students then measured the lengths again and calculated the percentage change in length. Their results are shown in the table below.

Temperature/°C	Initial length/mm	Final length/mm	Change in length/mm	% change in length
35	50	57.3	7.3	+14.6
25	50	53.4	3.4	+6.8
5	50	51.8	1.8	

a) Calculate the percentage change in length of the potato cylinder kept at 5° C.   [2]

....

....

....

....

b) Explain the trend seen in the results.   [5]

....

....

....

....

....

c) Suggest a reason why temperatures higher than 35° C were not used.   [1]

....

....

....

d) Suggest one way in which the strength of evidence from this experiment could be improved.   [1]

....

....

3   Two restaurant workers were preparing some carrots for cooking. They each placed a large batch of carrots into a pan and covered them in water. One worker added salt to the water for flavour, but the other did not. One hour later, the chef came to cook the carrots and noticed that one batch was no longer covered in water, but the other one was. The two pans were the same size, had the same number of carrots in them and the amount of water added was the same.

a) Which of the two batches was no longer covered in water?   [1]

....

....

b) Explain the differences in the water levels in the two pans.   [4]

....

....

....

....

....

[Total = ... /24 marks]

Further application

1 A chicken egg is a single large cell encased in a shell. The shell can be removed by leaving the raw egg in dilute acid for several days. This leaves the cell (egg) surrounded by a cell membrane.

A student used shelled eggs for an experiment on osmosis. They weighed three shelled eggs and placed one in distilled water, one in 5% salt solution, and one in 15% salt solution. They left them for 24 hours.

After this time, the egg in distilled water had burst. The student re-weighed the other two eggs. Both had lost weight.

a) Explain why the egg in distilled water had burst. [3]

....

....

....

....

....

b) The student calculated that the egg in 15% salt solution had lost 20% of its weight. Suggest what the percentage weight change of the egg in 5% salt solution was. Choose from the four possibilities below by underlining your choice. [1]

    A   −10%

    B   −25%

    C   +2%

    D   −20%

c) The experiment investigated the process of osmosis. Explain the term osmosis in the context of this experiment. [3]

....

....

....

....

....

....

2 Rock pools on rocky shores contain salt water (a solution of sodium chloride). At low tide on summer days, the heat causes some of the water to evaporate, but the rock pools do not dry up.

a) Explain why the evaporation of some of the water could be a danger to the animals living in the rock pool. [4]

....

....

....

....

....

Biology

b) River estuaries contain salt water at high tide, but fresh water at low tide. Estuaries tend to have a very low biodiversity – few species live there, although the populations of the species that do are often large.

i) Suggest why very few species live in estuaries. **[3]**

....

....

....

....

ii) Suggest why the populations of these species are often large. **[1]**

....

....

3 A scientist was doing an experiment on the effect of temperature on osmosis. Ten identical cubes of potato were weighed and placed in each of six beakers of water and left for 24 hours. Each beaker was placed in a water bath at different temperatures. After 24 hours the cubes were removed, blotted dry and re-weighed. The percentage increase in weight was calculated. The results are shown in the table below.

Temperature/°C	% change in mass
10	5
20	13
30	26
40	32
50	8
60	2

a) Plot the results on the graph paper. **[4]**

[Total = ... /19 marks]

Required practical 3: Testing for carbohydrates, lipids and proteins

In this practical you will test a range of foods for the presence of **carbohydrates**, **lipids** and **proteins**. The tests are the Benedict's test for reducing sugars, the iodine test for starch, the Biuret test for proteins and the emulsion test for lipids. These are **qualitative** tests which simply indicate the presence of the substance tested for, not the quantity of it in the sample.

Aim

Use qualitative reagents to test for a range of carbohydrates, lipids and proteins.

Equipment and reagents

- Three samples of food to be tested
- Pestle and mortar
- Filter funnel and filter paper
- Five 100 cm³ beakers
- Conical flask
- Distilled water
- Four test tubes
- Graduated pipette
- Labels or marker pen

- Electric water bath or beaker of water and Bunsen burner
- Benedict's solution
- Iodine solution (0.01 mol/dm³)
- Ethanol
- Biuret solutions A (1% copper sulfate) and B (1% potassium hydroxide or sodium hydroxide)

Method

1 Select three samples of food.
2 Take one sample and grind it with a small quantity of water in the mortar, using the pestle.
3 Pour off the liquid into a test tube, leaving any solids behind.
4 Label the test tube with the name of the food used.
5 Repeat for the other two samples.
6 Carry out the tests below on the three food samples.

Part A: Iodine test for starch

1 Add some sample solution to a test tube.
2 Using the graduated pipette, add two drops of iodine solution to the food sample.
3 Record your observations in the table in question 1 on page 13.

Part B: Benedict's test for reducing sugars

1 Half-fill a beaker with water.
2 Place the beaker on a tripod over a Bunsen burner, or heat the water using an electric water bath, until the water boils.
3 Add some sample solution to a test tube.
4 Add an equal volume of Benedict's solution to the test tube and swirl the mixture.
5 Place the test tube in the water bath for about 5 minutes, or until the colour of the mixture no longer changes.
6 Observe and record any colour changes during that time, and record the final colour in the table in question 1 on page 13.

Part C: Biuret test for protein

1 Add some sample solution to a test tube.
2 Add an equal volume of Biuret solution A to the sample.
3 Add a few drops of Biuret solution B to the test tube.
4 Record your observations in the table in question 1 on page 13.

Part D: Emulsion test for lipids

1 Add some sample solution to a test tube.
2 Add 2 cm³ of ethanol to the sample.
3 Add 2 cm³ of distilled water to the mixture, and gently shake the solution.
4 Record your observations in the table in question 1 on page 13.

Further information can be found in **AQA GCSE (9–1) Combined Science Student Book** on pages:
- 44–46: Functions of the parts of the digestive system
- 46–48: Human digestive enzymes
- 66: Visking tubing.

Key terms

Carbohydrate: a group of organic compounds that includes sugars, starch and cellulose. They contain carbon, hydrogen and oxygen.

Lipids: a group of organic compounds that are oily to the touch and insoluble in water. Lipids include fatty acids, oils, waxes and triglycerides (fats).

Proteins: a group of organic compounds that are large molecules composed of one or more long chains of amino acids.

Qualitative test: a test that indicates the presence or absence of a substance, but gives no information about its quantity.

Health and safety

- Wear eye protection.
- Ethanol (both liquid and vapour) is highly flammable and should be kept away from a lit Bunsen burner. It is also harmful if swallowed.
- Biuret solutions contain copper sulfate and sodium hydroxide. Copper sulfate is harmful if swallowed, and can cause skin irritation and serious eye damage, so must be handled with care. See CLEAPSS hazard 27C. Sodium hydroxide is corrosive, so the solution should be handled with care. See CLEAPSS hazcard 91A. Wipe up any spillages, and if they do come into contact with skin, wash the skin immediately.

Tips

- Part A: If starch is present, a blue-black colour will appear.
- Part B: If an electric water bath at 80 °C is available, miss out steps 1–2.
- Reducing sugar causes the Benedict's solution to change from blue – to green – to orange – to brick red.
- Part C: If protein is present, there will be a colour change from blue to purple.
- Part D: If lipid is present, a milky-white emulsion will form.

Observations

1 Record your observations for each of the tests in the table below:

Food sample	Iodine test		Benedict's test		Biuret test		Emulsion test	
	Final colour	Starch present? (Y/N)	Final colour	Sugar present? (Y/N)	Final colour	Protein present? (Y/N)	Final colour	Lipid present? (Y/N)

2 What would a negative result for the Biuret test look like?

....

....

Conclusions

3 A negative result in the Benedict's test does not prove that no sugars are present in the food. Explain why.

....

....

....

....

Evaluation

4 Some foods (e.g. orange juice) produce results in these tests that can be difficult to interpret. Suggest why.

....

....

....

....

5 A quantitative test gives a measurement of the amount of a substance present. A qualitative test just tells you whether the substance is present or not. The Benedict's test is sometimes described as semi-quantitative. Explain why.

....

....

....

....

Exam-style questions

1 Plant seeds always contain a food store. This provides the germinating seed with energy to grow until it breaks the soil surface and is able to photosynthesise. This food store is often either starch or protein in different seeds. The diagram below shows a section of a broad bean seed with its food store.

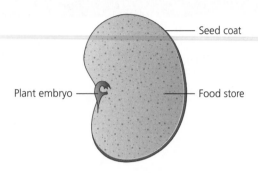

a) Why would the growing plant be unable to carry out photosynthesis before it broke through the surface of the soil? **[1]**

....

....

b) Describe in detail how a scientist could test whether the food store was composed of starch or protein (or a mixture of the two). The food store in the broad bean is a solid. **[6]**

....

....

....

....

....

....

....

....

....

....

....

....

....

....

2 Complete the table below about tests for different food substances. **[6]**

Name of test	Substance tested for	Colour change indicating positive result
Iodine test		
	Protein	
		Blue – green – orange – brick red

Biology

3 Four food samples were tested for sugar, lipids, starch and proteins. The results are shown in the table below.

| Sample | Final colour of test | | | |
	Iodine test	Benedict's test	Biuret test	Emulsion test
A	Blue-black	Brick red	Blue	Colourless
B	Orange-brown	Green	Blue	Colourless
C	Blue-black	Blue	Blue	Milky white
D	Orange-brown	Orange	Purple	Colourless

a) Which food types were present in these samples?

i) Sample A [1]

....

iii) Sample C [1]

....

ii) Sample B [1]

....

iv) Sample D [1]

....

b) What conclusions would you draw from the Benedict's test results? [3]

....

....

....

c) A qualitative test only gives information about the presence or absence of a factor. A quantitative test gives a measurement of quantity. Suggest why the Benedict's test can be described as semi-quantitative. [2]

....

....

....

4 Describe the stages involved in testing a sample of cake for the presence of glucose and describe the appearance of a positive and a negative result. [6]

....

....

....

....

....

....

....

....

5 The iodine test is an example of a qualitative test. Explain the meaning of this term. [2]

....

....

....

[Total = ... /30 marks]

Further application

1 Visking tubing acts like a partially permeable membrane, letting small molecules through but preventing the passage of large molecules. A student set up an experiment as shown below.

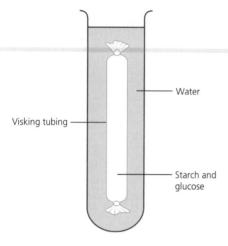

Water

Visking tubing

Starch and glucose

The apparatus was left for 24 hours. The solutions inside and outside the Visking tubing were then tested for starch and glucose. The solution inside the Visking tubing gave a positive result for both starch and glucose.

a) How would the student test for starch? [2]

....

....

....

b) How would the student test for glucose? [3]

....

....

....

....

....

....

....

c) What would the results have been for these tests on the solution outside the Visking tubing? [2]

....

....

....

d) Explain your answer to part c). [1]

....

....

e) State the process by which substances (other than water) move through the Visking tubing. [1]

....

Biology

f) This apparatus is sometimes used as a model for the working of the human gut, with the Visking tubing modelling the lining of the gut.

i) What would the water represent in this model of the gut? **[1]**

....

ii) State one way in which Visking tubing is an accurate model of the gut lining, and one way in which it is not. **[2]**

....

....

....

2 A quantitative test gives a measurement indicating the amount of a substance present. A qualitative test just indicates whether a substance is present. The Benedict's test can be used to compare the amount of glucose in two samples, without giving an actual measurement. Suggest a modification of the Benedict's test that would produce a numerical result, and so give a fully quantitative result. **[2]**

....

....

....

....

3 The Benedict's test is a test for sugars, but some sugars (called non-reducing sugars) do not give a positive result. However, boiling non-reducing sugars with dilute hydrochloric acid before doing the test converts them into reducing sugars, which will give a positive result.

a) When testing for non-reducing sugars, the normal Benedict's test is always done first. State the reason for this. **[1]**

....

....

....

b) A sample contains a mixture of reducing and non-reducing sugars. The presence of the reducing sugars means that a Benedict's test will always be positive. Suggest a way in which you could detect the presence of non-reducing sugars in the sample. **[4]**

....

....

....

....

....

....

....

....

[Total = .../19 marks]

Required practical 4: Investigating the effect of pH on amylase

In this practical you will investigate the effect of **pH** on the activity of amylase **enzyme**. Amylase catalyses the breakdown of starch into maltose and is found in saliva and pancreatic juice. The reaction is followed by monitoring the rate of breakdown of starch, using iodine solution to test for the presence of starch in the reaction mixture.

Aim

Investigate the effect of pH on the rate of reaction of amylase enzyme.

Equipment and reagents

- 10 test tubes
- Test tube rack
- Electric water bath, or a Bunsen burner and beaker, at 35°C
- Spotting tile
- 5 cm³ measuring cylinder
- Pasteur pipettes, syringes or 5 cm³ measuring cylinders
- Stopwatch
- Starch solution (1%)
- Fungal amylase solution (0.1%)
- Labelled buffered solutions at pH 4, 5, 6 and 7
- Labels
- Iodine solution (0.01 M)
- Thermometer

Method

1 Prepare a water bath at 35°C (electrical, or Bunsen burner and beaker).

Note

If using a beaker of water as a water bath, use the thermometer to check that the temperature is maintained at 35°C (+/– 2°C).

2 Place a single drop of iodine solution into each well on the spotting tile.
3 Label a test tube with the pH to be tested.
4 Place 2 cm³ of amylase into the test tube.
5 Add 1 cm³ of buffer solution to the test tube.
6 Place in the water bath and leave to equilibrate for 1 minute (approximately).
7 Add 2 cm³ of starch to the amylase/buffer solution and start the stopwatch.
8 Mix using a plastic pipette.
9 After 10 seconds, use the plastic pipette to place one drop of the mixture on the first drop of iodine. The iodine solution should turn blue-black.
10 Return the rest of the solution back into the test tube.
11 Wait a further 10 seconds. Remove a second drop of the mixture to add to the next drop of iodine.
12 Repeat step 11 until the iodine solution and the amylase/buffer/starch mixture remain orange. This indicates that the starch has been completely broken down.

Tip

If the iodine solution turns orange immediately, the reaction is going too fast. Speak to your teacher – you may need to dilute the amylase solution.

13 Count how many iodine drops you have used, each one equalling 10 seconds of reaction time. Record this time.
14 Repeat the whole procedure with another of the pH buffers, until you have used all four of the buffers provided.

Further information can be found in the **AQA GCSE (9–1) Combined Science Student Book** on pages:
- 49–50: Denaturing of enzymes
- 50: Digestive (breakdown) and synthesis enzymes.

Key terms

pH: a measure of the acidity or alkalinity of a solution.

Enzyme: a biological catalyst, which speeds up the rate of a given reaction without taking part in it.

Health and safety

- Wear eye protection.
- Amylase solution and iodine solution are low hazard once made up. Wear eye protection when handling iodine solution. Iodine solution may stain skin or clothing.

Maths opportunities

- Division
- Translating information between graphical and numeric form
- Carrying out rate calculations for chemical reactions

Observations

1 Plot a graph of reaction rate (1/time) against pH.

> **Tip**
>
> It is better to plot 1/time (reaction rate) on the *y*-axis rather than just time, as it makes the graph 'the right way up' (i.e. when the reaction goes faster, the line goes upwards).

2 Describe and explain any trend seen in your results.

....

....

....

Conclusions

3 Estimate the optimum pH for fungal amylase.

....

....

....

Evaluation

4 Explain why it is necessary to control the temperature in this experiment.

....

....

5 Evaluate the strength of evidence for your estimation of the optimum pH.

....

....

....

....

Exam-style questions

1 Scientists did an experiment to find the optimum pH of the enzyme pepsin. Pepsin is a protease, which is an enzyme that breaks down proteins into amino acids, found in the stomach of mammals. The results are shown below.

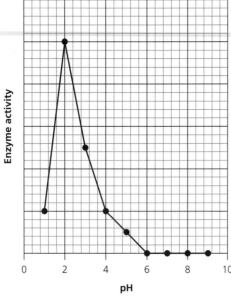

a) Estimate the optimum pH for pepsin. [1]

....

b) Suggest one modification to the experimental procedure that would give a more accurate estimate of the optimum pH. [1]

....

....

....

c) Suggest three factors that the scientists would need to control in this experiment. [3]

....

....

....

d) The optimum pH for pepsin is lower than for most enzymes. Suggest one reason for this. [2]

....

....

e) Suggest one reason for the results obtained at pH values 6 to 9. [1]

....

....

2 A student was planning to do an experiment on the effect of temperature on an enzyme. They planned to control the pH and the concentration of the enzyme.

a) State one other factor that the student should control in this experiment. [1]

....

b) How could they control the pH? [2]

....

....

c) Enzymes have different optimum pH values. Describe a preliminary experiment the student would need to do if they were to control the pH at the correct value. **[2]**

....

....

....

d) Suggest the range of temperatures that the student should use when testing the effect of temperature on the enzyme. **[2]**

....

3 Enzymes have an optimum pH value at which they work best, but this value varies in different enzymes. Some of the bonds in an enzyme molecule are stable at a particular pH, but when the pH is a long way from the optimum, they break. This can result in the enzyme becoming denatured.

a) Explain how the breaking of bonds in the enzyme can cause it to denature. **[3]**

....

....

....

....

....

....

b) Suggest an explanation for the different optimum pH values of different enzymes. **[3]**

....

....

....

....

4 The breakdown of proteins into amino acids can be followed using albumen solution. Albumen is a protein, and albumen solution is cloudy. When the protein is broken down, the solution goes clear.

Describe how you would carry out an experiment to test the effect of pH on protease. Include details of control variables and the range of pH values that you would use. **[6]**

....

....

....

....

....

....

....

....

....

....

....

....

[Total = ... /27 marks]

Further application

1   It is very difficult to make pineapple jelly. Jelly sets due to the formation of bonds between protein fibres in gelatine. Pineapple contains a mixture of protease enzymes called bromelain, which breaks these bonds as they form, and so the jelly never sets. The problem can be overcome by using tinned pineapple, which has been heated during the canning process, instead of fresh. Bromelain can also cause problems for some people after eating fresh pineapple. They experience a sore mouth and/or tongue, and if they eat pineapple regularly they may even develop mouth ulcers.

a) What does the term protease mean?   [1]

....

....

b) Explain why heating the pineapple during the canning process allows the use of the fruit to make jelly.   [4]

....

....

....

....

....

....

....

....

c) Suggest one reason why some people experience sore mouths after eating fresh pineapple.   [1]

....

....

d) Suggest a reason why bromelain causes problems in the mouth, but never affects the stomach.   [2]

....

....

....

2   Many plants do not grow well when the pH of the soil is below 5. There are many reasons for this, but one is that the growth of nitrogen-fixing bacteria in the soil is reduced by low pH. Nitrogen-fixing bacteria convert nitrogen into nitrates, which are necessary for plant growth. The growth of the bacteria may be inhibited by low pH because some of their enzymes could be denatured. The bacterial populations survive in acidic soils but grow slowly.

a) What group of chemicals, essential for growth, requires nitrogen?   [1]

....

b) Growth requires energy. Suggest why the denaturing of certain enzymes in the bacteria can result in lack of growth.   [2]

....

....

....

Biology

c) Explain the process by which an enzyme becomes denatured. [3]

....

....

....

....

....

3 Meat tenderisers contain enzymes that break down protein links in the meat fibres, so the fibres become looser and the meat is more tender. Meat tenderiser is applied to the meat an hour or so before cooking. It is best to leave the meat outside the fridge during this time.

a) The enzymes in meat tenderiser have a low specificity. Explain the meaning of this term. [1]

....

....

....

b) Explain why it is best to apply the tenderiser an hour before cooking the meat (even if the cooking time is quite long). [2]

....

....

....

....

c) Explain the reason why it is recommended that the meat is not left in the fridge during the tenderisation period. [2]

....

....

....

....

....

[Total = ... /19 marks]

Required practical 5: Investigating the effect of light intensity on photosynthesis

In this practical you will investigate the effect of **light intensity** on the rate of **photosynthesis** in pondweed. The oxygen-enriched air that is given off as a result of photosynthesis is collected and measured to allow a calculation of the rate of photosynthesis. Light intensity is varied by moving a lamp closer to the plant.

Aim

Investigate the effect of light intensity on the rate of photosynthesis using an aquatic organism such as pondweed.

Equipment and reagents

- 250 cm³ beaker
- Filter funnel
- 1 cm³ measuring cylinder
- Freshly cut 10 cm piece of pondweed
- Light source/lamp
- Metre rule
- Stopwatch
- Plasticine
- 1% sodium hydrogen carbonate solution

Method

1 The experiment should be carried out in a darkened room.

2 Fill the beaker about three-quarters full with sodium hydrogen carbonate solution.

3 Assemble the apparatus as shown below, but do not place the measuring cylinder in the beaker yet.

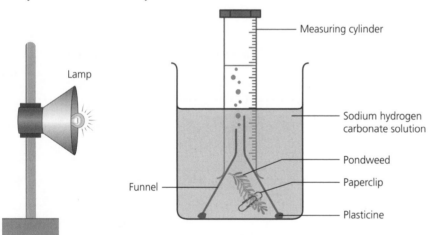

4 Place the lamp 20 cm away from the beaker.

5 Wait for 5 minutes, or until bubbles can be seen rising from the pondweed.

6 Fill the measuring cylinder with sodium hydrogen carbonate solution and invert over the funnel.

7 Start the stopwatch.

8 Leave for 2 minutes and record the volume of gas collected.

9 Record the results in the table in the **observations** section.

10 Repeat the count two more times. This will allow the mean volume of gas collected per minute to be calculated.

11 Move the lamp to a distance of 40 cm from the beaker and repeat steps 7 to 10.

12 Repeat at distances of 60 cm and 80 cm between the beaker and the light source.

13 Plot a graph of volume of gas collected against 1/distance of lamp in question 2 of the **observations** section.

Further information can be found in the **AQA GCSE (9–1) Combined Science Student Book** on pages:
- 96–97: Photosynthetic reaction
- 97–99: Rate of photosynthesis.

Key terms

Light intensity: the brightness of a light.

Photosynthesis: the process by which green plants make food, using carbon dioxide, water and light energy.

Health and safety

- Wear eye protection.
- The combination of wet hands and electricity can result in shock. Do not handle the lamp with wet hands.
- If the floor gets wet, you may slip. Mop up any spills immediately.

Maths opportunities

- Division
- Calculating means
- Translating information between graphical and numeric form
- Understanding and using inverse proportion (the inverse square law)
- Using fractions

Key equations

$$\text{carbon dioxide} + \text{water} \xrightarrow{\text{light}} \text{glucose} + \text{oxygen}$$

Notes

- Some versions of this experiment add water instead of sodium hydrogen carbonate solution, but in this version sodium hydrogen carbonate is added to ensure that the plant has enough carbon dioxide to photosynthesise. If carbon dioxide is a limiting factor, light intensity will have no effect on the plant.
- The plasticine ensures that the water (and its contained carbon dioxide) can circulate, so that the plant has access to all the water in the beaker.

Tip

If you see no bubbles at all, speak to your teacher. The plant may need to be replaced.

Tip

Even though the measuring cylinder is upside down, record your results using the bottom of the meniscus as usual.

Biology

Observations

1 a) Record your results in the table below.

Distance of lamp/cm	1/distance of lamp/a.u.	Volume of gas collected in minutes/cm³
20		
40		
60		
80		

   b) Plot a graph of volume of gas collected against 1/distance of the lamp.

   c) Describe any trend seen in your results.

   ....

   ....

   ....

   ....

   ....

2 From observing the experiment, can you identify a source of possible inaccuracy in the results?

   ....

   ....

   ....

Conclusions

3 Explain the pattern of results you have obtained.

....

....

....

Evaluation

4 Explain the purpose of using sodium hydrogen carbonate in this experiment.

....

....

5 Explain why the funnel was raised off the bottom of the beaker (by the plasticine).

....

....

....

....

....

6 This experiment is sometimes done by counting the bubbles given off from the pondweed every minute, instead of collecting and measuring the volume of gas. Explain why this would give less accurate results.

....

....

....

....

Biology

Exam-style questions

1 The diagram below shows the results of an experiment on the effect of light intensity on rate of photosynthesis at two different temperatures.

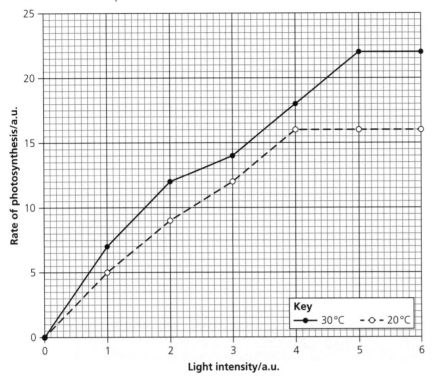

a) Describe the differences between the results at 20 °C and 30 °C.   [3]

....

....

....

b) Suggest a reason for the higher rate of photosynthesis at 30 °C.   [2]

....

....

(HT) c) Explain why the rate of photosynthesis levelled off at high light intensities.   [1]

....

....

2 The diagram below shows an experiment to test the effect of light intensity on the rate of photosynthesis. The light was set at different distances from the plant, and the number of bubbles given off per minute was recorded.

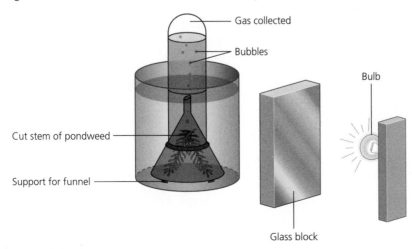

a) Suggest one reason why the results might be inaccurate. [1]

....

....

b) Suggest one way in which the experiment might be improved to remove the source of inaccuracy. [1]

....

....

c) Suggest a reason why the experiment was carried out in a darkened room. [1]

....

....

d) Explain the purpose of the glass block. [2]

....

....

....

HT 3 A student carried out an experiment on the effect of light intensity on the production of gas by pondweed. The results are shown below.

Distance of light/m	Light intensity/a.u.	Volume of gas collected per minute/cm³
1.0	1.0	1.3
0.8	1.6	2.5
0.6	2.8	3.6
0.4	6.3	5.4
0.2	25	5.5
0.1		5.6

a) The light intensity was calculated from the distance using the inverse square law. Use this law to calculate the missing value for 0.1 m. [2]

....

....

....

b) The plant was provided with excess carbon dioxide and a suitable temperature. Suggest the factor that was limiting photosynthesis at the higher light intensities. [1]

....

....

[Total = ... /14 marks]

Biology

Further application

1 Experiments were carried out on the effect of light intensity on photosynthesis at different temperatures and carbon dioxide concentrations. The results are shown below.

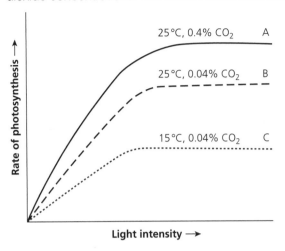

a) State the limiting factor at high light intensities in graph B and in graph C. Give reasons for your choices. **[4]**

Limiting factor in graph B:

....

Reason:

....

....

Limiting factor in graph C:

....

Reason:

....

....

....

b) The limiting factor at high light intensities is uncertain. Explain why. **[2]**

....

....

....

2 The graph below shows the rates of respiration and photosynthesis at different light intensities.

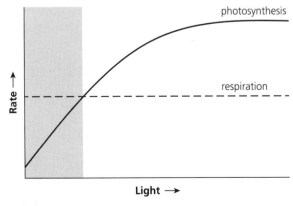

a) Explain the shape of the curve for photosynthesis. [2]

....

....

b) Explain the shape of the line for respiration. [1]

....

....

c) Suggest why plants might be unable to survive in locations where light intensity never exceeds values in the grey zone of the graph. [5]

....

....

....

....

....

3 In the horticultural industry, plants are grown in large greenhouses where various environmental factors can be controlled. The greenhouses can be lit; burners can generate carbon dioxide, which can be pumped into the greenhouse; the greenhouse can be heated and ventilation can be adjusted to control the temperature. Light intensity, temperature and carbon dioxide concentration are all limiting factors for photosynthesis.

a) Put ticks in the table below to show which factors would need to be altered in the conditions shown. [3]

Situation	Heating to be used	Lighting to be used	Carbon dioxide to be added
Warm summer day			
Warm summer night			
Cold winter day			

b) Plants grown in enhanced levels of carbon dioxide have been shown to be heavier than those grown in normal levels of carbon dioxide. Explain the reason for this. [4]

....

....

....

....

When carbon dioxide levels are enhanced, farmers have to add more nitrogenous fertiliser to the soil.

c) What role does nitrogen play in the growth of plants? [2]

....

....

....

d) Explain why more nitrogen is needed when extra carbon dioxide is supplied. [1]

....

....

....

[Total = ... /24 marks]

Biology

Required practical 6: Investigating the effect of practice on reaction time

In this practical you will investigate the effect of a factor – in this case, practice – on human reaction time. Reaction time will be measured by measuring the distance a dropped ruler falls before it is caught, with the distance then being converted into reaction time. The hypothesis being tested is that reaction time decreases with practice.

Aim

Plan and carry out an investigation into the effect of a factor on human reaction time.

Equipment and reagents

- Metre rule
- Chair
- Table

Method

1 Work in pairs. One of the pair is the tester and the other is the subject.
2 The subject should sit down on the chair and direct his or her eyes across the room, not looking down at their hand.
3 The subject's forearm should be placed across the table with their hand hanging over the edge of the table. The same arm should be used throughout the experiment.
4 The tester holds the ruler vertically so that the bottom 0 cm end hangs in between the subject's thumb and first finger (see the diagram below).

Further information can be found in the **AQA GCSE (9–1) Combined Science Student Book** on pages:
- 359–362: The human nervous system – structure and function (or *CS 2: 3–6*)
- 362–363: Effect of a factor on human reaction time (or *CS 2: 6–7*).

Health and safety

No significant hazards.

Maths opportunities
- Division
- Calculating means
- Translating information between graphical and numerical forms

Key equations

$$\text{mean} = \frac{\text{sum of results}}{\text{total number of results}}$$

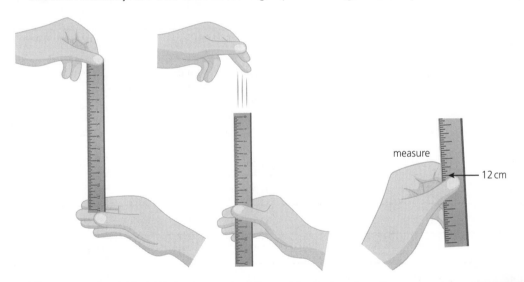

measure

— 12 cm

5 The tester should hold the ruler against the subject's hand so the zero mark is level with the top of the thumb. The subject's finger and thumb should be touching the ruler.
6 Without warning, the tester then drops the ruler and the subject attempts to catch it as quickly as possible.
7 Record the distance travelled by measuring where the ruler was caught, just above the subject's thumb (see the diagram above).
8 After a short break, repeat the drop test nine more times.
9 Use the table on page 32 to convert the distances into reaction times. Record your results in the table on page 33, found in the **observations** section.
10 If time allows, repeat the experiment two more times.
11 Plot your results of mean reaction time against trial number on the graph paper provided in the **observations** section.

Tip

An alternative for lining up the thumb is to draw a line on the thumbnail in thin marker pen, and align the zero mark with that.

Distance ruler falls/cm	Reaction time/s	Distance ruler falls/cm	Reaction time/s	Distance ruler falls/cm	Reaction time/s	Distance ruler falls/cm	Reaction time/s
1	0.05	26	0.23	51	0.32	76	0.39
2	0.06	27	0.23	52	0.33	77	0.40
3	0.08	28	0.24	53	0.33	78	0.40
4	0.09	29	0.24	54	0.33	79	0.40
5	0.10	30	0.25	55	0.34	80	0.40
6	0.11	31	0.25	56	0.34	81	0.41
7	0.12	32	0.26	57	0.34	82	0.41
8	0.13	33	0.26	58	0.34	83	0.41
9	0.14	34	0.26	59	0.35	84	0.41
10	0.14	35	0.27	60	0.35	85	0.42
11	0.15	36	0.27	61	0.35	86	0.42
12	0.16	37	0.28	62	0.36	87	0.42
13	0.16	38	0.28	63	0.36	88	0.42
14	0.17	39	0.28	64	0.36	89	0.43
15	0.18	40	0.29	65	0.36	90	0.43
16	0.18	41	0.29	66	0.37	91	0.43
17	0.19	42	0.29	67	0.37	92	0.43
18	0.19	43	0.30	68	0.37	93	0.44
19	0.20	44	0.30	69	0.38	94	0.44
20	0.21	45	0.30	70	0.38	95	0.44
21	0.21	46	0.31	71	0.38	96	0.44
22	0.22	47	0.31	72	0.38	97	0.45
23	0.22	48	0.31	73	0.39	98	0.45
24	0.22	49	0.32	74	0.39	99	0.45
25	0.23	50	0.32	75	0.39	100	0.45

Biology

Observations

1 Record your results in the table below.

| Trial number | Reaction time/s | | | |
	Experiment 1	Experiment 2	Experiment 3	Mean
1				
2				
3				
4				
5				
6				
7				
8				
9				
10				

2 Plot the mean results on the graph paper below. Choose a type of graph appropriate to the data.

3 Describe any trend seen in your results.

....

....

....

....

....

....

Conclusions

4 Do your results support the hypothesis that reaction time decreases with practice? Give reasons for your decision.

....

....

....

....

....

....

....

Evaluation

5 Compare your results with those of other students. Are the results reproducible? Justify your answer.

....

....

....

....

6 In this experiment, we happened to have controlled the subject of the test (i.e. the person doing it). This is not actually good practice in this instance. Explain why.

....

....

....

....

7 Suggest one other way in which the method could be improved.

....

....

....

....

Biology

Exam-style questions

1 An experiment was done to compare the reaction times of males and females. Subjects had to press a button when a certain shape was flashed on a screen, and their reaction time was measured. The results were as follows.

Trial number	Reaction times/s			
	Male 1	Male 2	Female 1	Female 2
1	0.15	0.22	0.11	0.09
2	0.21	0.24	0.35	0.23
3	0.23	0.15	0.22	0.11
4	0.16	0.26	0.18	0.28
5	0.18	0.19	0.26	0.14
6	0.22	0.21	0.23	0.14
7	0.24	0.14	0.17	0.29
8	0.15	0.18	0.27	0.27
9	0.19	0.12	0.21	0.28
10	0.21	0.22	0.18	0.14
Mean	0.19		0.22	0.20

a) Calculate the mean reaction time of Male 2. **[1]**

....

b) Which of the following conclusions best fits the data? Underline your answer and give a reason for your choice. **[2]**

A Males react faster than females.

B Females react faster than males.

C There is no difference in the reaction times of males and females.

Reason:

....

....

....

....

....

c) One scientist suggested that they ought to carry out more trials per individual. State one way in which this would improve the quality of the data. **[1]**

....

....

....

d) Apart from the number of trials per individual, state two other weaknesses in the strength of evidence from this experiment. **[2]**

....

....

....

....

....

e) Explain why the response to the shape on the screen in this test is not classed as a reflex action. **[1]**

....[Total = .../............

....

....

2 The reaction time of a sprinter can be important. If an athlete can respond faster to the sound of the starting gun, he or she can gain a significant advantage over competitors. A group of five athletes underwent a training programme to try to improve their reaction times. For an hour every day for a month they sat in front of a computer screen that flashed a light on screen at unpredictable intervals. The athletes had to press a button when they saw the light. Their mean reaction time was tested before and after the training, and the results compared. The results are shown below.

The average reaction time for humans is 0.25 seconds to a visual stimulus, 0.17 for an audio stimulus and 0.15 seconds for a touch stimulus.

The people in charge of the programme decided that the results were inconclusive.

a) What was the maximum decrease in reaction time shown by any of the athletes? **[1]**

....

b) Describe one piece of evidence in the data that suggests that the training might improve reaction time. **[1]**

....

....

c) Describe one piece of evidence in the data that suggests that the training might not improve reaction time. **[1]**

....

....

d) Suggest why this study may not be valid when applied to responding to a starting pistol. **[2]**

....

....

....

....

....

....

[Total = .../12 marks]

Biology

Further application

1   A study was carried out on the effects of alcohol on reaction time in 200 people. The results are shown below:

% blood alcohol concentration	Mean reaction time/milliseconds
0	25
0.02	38
0.05	68
0.08	120

a) Explain why drinking alcohol before driving increases the risk of an accident.   [1]

....

....

....

....

b) In England and Wales, the current drink-drive limit is 0.035%. In Scotland, the limit has been lowered to 0.022%. Suggest why some people believe that the drink-drive limit should be lowered to 0.   [1]

....

....

....

....

c) Suggest one reason why the strength of evidence from this study is strong.   [1]

....

....

....

....

d) Calculate the percentage increase in reaction time with a blood concentration of 0.05% alcohol, compared to a person who has not drunk any alcohol.   [2]

....

....

....

2   Animals react to a range of stimuli. Some of these responses are very rapid and are called reflex actions. In a reflex, the nerve impulse travels along sensory neurones to the central nervous system. Each sensory neurone then connects to a relay neurone across a small gap, called a synapse. After a short delay, the impulse travels along the relay neurone, across another synapse (with another short delay) and then down a motor neurone to the effector, which performs the action.

a) Apart from its rapid speed, what is the other characteristic of a reflex action?   [1]

....

b) Place ticks in the table below to indicate which of the actions described are reflex actions. **[3]**

Blinking	
Breathing	
Stepping away from an oncoming vehicle	
A goalkeeper saving a shot in a football match	
Sneezing	
Speaking	

c) From the description of a reflex action in the passage, suggest a reason why reflexes are so rapid compared to voluntary actions. **[2]**

....

....

....

....

d) It is possible to learn a new reflex action. Saliva is normally produced as a reflex when food is smelled or seen, but if a bell is rung every time a dog is given food, the animal will eventually produce saliva when a bell is rung, even if there is no food. Scientists have used this as evidence that the nervous system can form new synapses in the central nervous system as a response to learning. Explain how the experiment provides this evidence. **[3]**

....

....

....

....

....

....

....

....

[Total = .../14 marks]

Required practical 7: Investigating population size

There are two parts to this investigation:

A Investigating the population size of a plant species using **random sampling** with **quadrats**. The population of daisies in a school field is used in this example.

B Investigating the effect of trampling on plant distribution using a **transect** line. The distribution of plants on and around a trampled path through grass is used in this example.

Aim

Part A: Estimate the population of daisies in a school field.

Part B: Investigate the effect of trampling on the distribution of a species in a patch of grassland.

Equipment and reagents

- Quadrat (50 × 50 cm)
- 30 m tape measure

Key equation

$$\text{estimated population size} = \frac{\text{total area}}{\text{area sampled}} \times \text{number of plants counted}$$

Method

Part A: Estimate the population of daisies in a school field

1 You will need to work in groups of two or three.
2 Your teacher will have two bags containing cards/balls with numbers on them. Collect two numbers, one from each bag.

Note

The numbers represent the coordinates of a grid that your teacher has divided the area to be sampled into.

3 Use the numbers and the two pre-laid tape measures marking out the area to be studied to locate the first position for your quadrat.
4 Lay the quadrat on the ground.
5 Replace the numbers in the bags.
6 Count and record the number of the chosen species – in this example daisies – inside the quadrat.
7 Repeat steps 2–6 until you have recorded the numbers of the chosen plant species in ten different quadrats.
8 The total study area is 20 m × 20 m. Estimate the population of daisies using the estimated population size equation.

Part B: Investigate the effect of trampling on the distribution of a species in a patch of grassland

Your teacher will show you the plant you are to investigate.

1 Put the 30 m tape measure in a line across a trampled path in grassland, with the path crossing the line at roughly 15 m along the tape measure.
2 Put the quadrat against the transect line. One corner of the quadrat should touch the 0 m mark on the tape measure.
3 Count the number of plants inside the quadrat.
4 Repeat steps 2 and 3 at 1 m intervals along the transect.
5 Record your results in the table in the **observations** section. You should shade the boxes that correspond to where the transect is on the path.

Further information can be found in the **AQA GCSE (9–1) Combined Science Student Book** on pages:

- 445–447: Sampling (or CS 2: 88–91)
- 448–449: Measuring the population size of a plant species using random sampling (or CS 2: 92–93).

Key terms

Random sampling: samples that are taken randomly to avoid human influence or bias.

Quadrat: a frame of a specified area.

Transect: a surveying technique that samples at points distributed along a line or a narrow band.

Health and safety

Possible hazards when working on an area of grass include wet grass that could be slipped on and the possibility of hazardous material such as broken glass being present.

Maths opportunities

- Multiplication/division
- Estimates of population size based on sampling
- Calculating means
- Calculating area
- Translating information between graphical and numeric form

Tip

You will need to be careful when distinguishing individual plants from each other. A plant may be branched and initially appear like more than one. Check that what you are calling individual plants have separate entry points into the soil.

Observations

1 Record your results from Part B in the table below.

Distance along transect/m	Number of plants		Distance along transect/m	Number of plants
0			15	
1			16	
2			17	
3			18	
4			19	
5			20	
6			21	
7			22	
8			23	
9			24	
10			25	
11			26	
12			27	
13			28	
14			29	

2 Describe how the abundance of your chosen species was related (or not) to the position of the path in Part B.

....

....

....

....

Conclusions

3 On the basis of your results in Part B, how resistant is your chosen species to trampling?

....

....

....

4 Some species of plant are only found in trampled areas. They are tolerant to trampling, but suggest why they may be absent from areas where there is no trampling.

....

....

....

....

Biology

Evaluation

5 Do you think that 10 quadrats were enough to give results that are representative of the whole area sampled in Part A? Give reasons for your answer.

....

....

....

....

....

....

6 Explain the purpose of the random sampling in Part A.

....

....

....

....

7 Suggest how the strength of evidence in Part B could be improved.

....

....

....

....

....

Exam-style questions

1 A group of scientists carried out a population survey of clover in an area of grass in a park. The overall area surveyed was 250 000 m². Quadrats that measured 0.5 × 0.5 m were used to take 100 samples. The total number of clover plants in the sample was 2650.

a) Estimate the total number of clover plants in the whole area of grass. Show your working.   [2]

b) The quadrats were placed randomly within the area. Why was this necessary?   [1]

c) The same group also did a survey in an equal-sized area of woodland. For that survey, they used 500 quadrats. Suggest why more quadrats were needed in woodland.   [2]

2 A transect was done at the edge of some woodland, to see the effect of light intensity on the distribution of five plant species. The samples were taken along a line from the edge of the woodland, where the light level was highest, to an area well inside the woodland, where it was quite dark. The results are shown below.

Species	Numbers of plants at stations					
	Lightest ⟶ Darkest					
	Station 1	Station 2	Station 3	Station 4	Station 5	Station 6
A	4	3	6	3	4	1
B	11	13	11	0	0	0
C	2	7	5	8	9	8
D	5	2	0	0	0	0
E	1	1	1	0	0	0

a) Which species was least tolerant of lack of light?   [1]

b) Why do plants need light?   [1]

c) Suggest a reason why some plants may grow in larger numbers where the light level is low.   [2]

d) The group doing the experiment decided that the results for species E were inconclusive. Suggest why. **[1]**

....

....

e) Which species would you expect to have the largest leaves? Give a reason for your answer. **[3]**

....

....

....

....

....

....

3 A group of students surveyed a field using quadrats to estimate the number of buttercup plants. They used a sample of 10 quadrats, and sampled by dropping the quadrat over their shoulder so that they could not see the area where the quadrat would land. When they presented their results, their teacher said that they had not taken enough samples, and that their sampling method was not random.

a) When sampling using quadrats, why is it important to have enough samples? **[1]**

....

....

....

b) State a reason why the sampling method was not random. **[1]**

....

....

....

c) Give one other way in which their sampling technique could produce inaccurate results. **[1]**

....

....

....

....

d) Suggest a better method to achieve random sampling. **[4]**

....

....

....

....

....

[Total = ... /20 marks]

Further application

1 Quadrats were placed at random locations in an area of National Park. The object was to estimate the total numbers of a plant species, *Caltha palustris* (the marsh marigold), and study its distribution. The marsh marigold thrives in damp conditions. The total study area is shown in the diagram below, with the positions of the quadrats used and the numbers found in each quadrat. The total area measured 200 m × 200 m. The size of each quadrat is 0.5 m × 0.5 m.

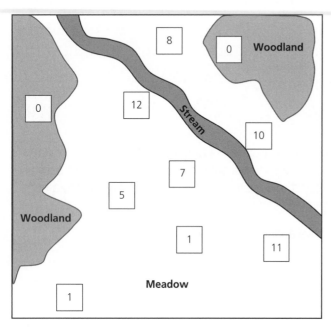

a) Use the data to estimate the number of marsh marigold plants in the total area. Show your working. [4]

....

....

....

....

....

....

....

b) Suggest two reasons why this estimate may be inaccurate. [2]

....

....

....

....

c) The scientists also wanted to estimate the number of ladybird beetles in the area. Suggest why the method used for the marsh marigold would not be appropriate. [1]

....

....

....

2 Scientists used transects to study the distribution of two woodland species, the ox-eye daisy and the sweet woodruff. They were interested in how the level of light and shade affected the distribution. They found that the ox-eye daisies were more common in sunny spots, and the sweet woodruff preferred partial shade.

a) Explain how the scientists would have set up and used transects for their study. **[3]**

....
....
....
....
....

The graph below shows how the balance of respiration and photosynthesis varies with light intensity in the two plants studied. The point at which respiration equals photosynthesis is called the compensation point, when there is no net uptake or release of carbon dioxide.

b) Estimate the compensation points for the two plants, A and B. **[2]**

A ....

B ....

c) Explain why a plant could not survive in a habitat where the light level never reached its compensation point. **[4]**

....
....
....
....
....
....

d) Identify which plant (A or B) is the sweet woodruff. Give reasons for your answer. **[3]**

....
....
....
....
....

[Total = .../19 marks]

Required practical 8: Preparing a pure, dry sample of a soluble salt

When a chemical reaction has finished, the product obtained is usually not pure. Sometimes, the reaction produces unwanted products or the reactants do not react fully. This means we end up with a mixture of the product we want, as well as unwanted chemicals (known as impurities). It is important to know a variety of separation techniques so that we can obtain pure samples of the products that we want.

Aim

Prepare a pure, dry sample of a soluble salt from an insoluble oxide or carbonate using a Bunsen burner to heat dilute acid and a water bath or electric heater to evaporate the solution.

In this practical you will react copper oxide powder with a solution of sulfuric acid. The reaction produces a solution of copper(II) sulfate and water.

> **Tip**
>
> The reaction is slow at room temperature, so the reaction mixture is heated to speed it up.

Equipment and reagents

- 25 cm³ measuring cylinder
- Two 100 cm³ conical flasks
- Weighing boat
- Spatula
- Two filter funnels with filter paper
- Bunsen burner, tripod, gauze and heatproof mat
- Evaporating dish
- Watch glass
- Mass balance (ideally measuring to 2 decimal places)
- 1.0 mol/dm³ sulfuric acid solution
- Copper(II) oxide powder
- Access to water

> **Tip**
>
> Read the method thoroughly before starting the experiment. If there is a step that you do not understand, ask your teascher for help before starting the experiment to avoid additional risk.

Method

1. Use a measuring cylinder to measure out 25 cm³ sulfuric acid solution. Pour this into a conical flask.
2. Use a mass balance to carefully weigh out approximately 2.00 g of copper oxide powder into a weighing boat. This is a small excess to ensure that all of the acid is reacted.
3. Carefully add the copper(II) oxide powder into the conical flask containing the sulfuric acid. Swirl to mix the reactants.
4. Gently heat the reaction mixture using the Bunsen burner. Do not allow the solution to boil.
5. Continue heating the solution for 5 minutes. If there is any black copper(II) oxide left, stop heating and allow the solution to cool. If the black copper(II) oxide disappears completely, use a spatula to carefully add some more, and heat the mixture for a further 2 minutes.
6. Use a filter funnel with filter paper above the second conical flask to filter the mixture; this removes the unreacted copper(II) oxide.

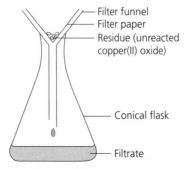

Filter funnel
Filter paper
Residue (unreacted copper(II) oxide)
Conical flask
Filtrate

Further information can be found in **AQA GCSE (9–1) Combined Science Student Book** on these pages:

- 137–140: Separating mixtures
- 214: Reaction of acids with metal oxides and metal carbonates
- 478–481: Factors affecting the rate of reactions (*or CS 2: 122–125*).

Health and safety ⚠

- Wear eye protection.
- Tell your teacher about any spills, do not try to clean them up yourself.
- Sulfuric acid solution is an irritant – you must wear eye protection and avoid getting acid (hot or cold) on your skin. Rinse well with water if this occurs.
- Copper (II) oxide powder is low hazard.
- Freshly boiled water can cause scalding. If scalded, hold the affected area under a cold running tap for at least 5 minutes.
- Do not allow the copper sulfate solution to boil dry during crystallisation. Thermal decomposition of the solid copper sulfate produces toxic sulfur dioxide and trioxide, which can lead to breathing difficulties.
- Ensure all electrical equipment is switched off at the mains until the solution is secured in the water bath or heater.

Maths opportunities   √2³+1

- Addition and subtraction
- Calculating percentages

> **Tip**
>
> Gentle heating means heating the reaction mixture with a Bunsen burner flame with the air-hole slightly open.

Chemistry

7 Transfer the solution from the conical flask into an evaporating basin.
8 Use a warm water bath or electric heater to gently heat the copper sulfate solution until crystals form around the edge of the solution.
9 Allow the solution to cool. Crystals of copper sulfate should form in the basin.
10 Use the mass balance to measure and record the mass of a watch glass.
11 Filter the crystals from the solution. Scrape them onto the watch glass. Allow them to dry.
12 Use the mass balance to measure and record the mass of the crystals and watch glass together.

Note

An alternative method to evaporate the water from the solution is to heat the solution with a Bunsen burner until the solution starts to boil. Once boiling, continue to gently heat the solution until crystals start to form around the edge of the solution.

Observations

1 Describe what you observe during the reaction between copper(II) oxide and sulfuric acid.

....
....
....
....
....
....
....
....

Tip

When describing observations during a reaction, first describe the appearance of the reactants (the chemicals present *before* the reaction has occurred) and then describe the appearance of the products (the chemicals formed *after* the reaction). These descriptions should include colour and physical state.

2 Explain your observations. Include chemical equations to support your explanation where appropriate.

....
....
....
....
....
....
....
....

3 Complete the following table.

Mass of watch glass / g	
Mass of watch glass and copper(II) sulfate crystals / g	
Mass of copper(II) sulfate crystals / g	

Conclusions

4 The theoretical maximum mass of copper sulfate in this experiment is 3.99 g.

Calculate your percentage yield.

[Percentage yield = ... %]

Evaluation

5 Use the percentage yield to evaluate your experiment. Include possible changes to the method that could increase yield.

Tip

When evaluating an experiment based on percentage yield, the yield is often too low or too high. If too low, consider where product may have been lost. If too high, consider where the experiment may have gained unwanted mass, or not lost enough mass.

Chemistry

Exam-style questions

1 Sulfuric acid is a strong acid.

    a) Suggest a pH value for sulfuric acid.   **[1]**

    ....

    b) Give the ionic equation for the neutralisation of an acid with an alkali.   **[3]**

    ....

2   **a)** One of the products of the neutralisation reaction between copper(II) oxide and sulfuric acid is copper(II) sulfate.

    Write a word equation for this reaction.   **[1]**

    ....

    b) Give the expected pH of the solution of copper sulfate, assuming that all of the sulfuric acid reacts with the copper(II) oxide.   **[1]**

    ....

    c) Write a balanced symbol equation for this reaction.   **[3]**

    ....

    d) Suggest an alternative reactant that could be used instead of copper(II) oxide that would form copper(II) sulfate when reacted with sulfuric acid.   **[1]**

    ....

    e) Copper(II) sulfate was formed from the reaction of an unknown green solid with sulfuric acid. The reaction formed a gaseous product that turned limewater milky.

    Write a word equation for the reaction between sulfuric acid and the unknown green solid.   **[2]**

    ....

3   **a)** Silver nitrate solution can be produced by reacting silver oxide with nitric acid.

    Write a word equation for this reaction.   **[1]**

    ....

    b) Complete the balanced symbol equation for this reaction.   **[1]**

    $..... Ag_2CO_3 + ... HNO_3 \rightarrow ..... AgNO_3 + ... + H_2O$

    c) Explain why an excess of silver oxide is needed during this reaction and **not** an excess of nitric acid.   **[3]**

    ....

    ....

    ....

    ....

    ....

Chemistry

d) Silver nitrate forms a colourless solution in water.

Why does this make it more difficult to determine whether or not the reaction is taking place when compared with the reaction between copper oxide and sulfuric acid? **[1]**

....

....

e) pH paper can be used to determine when the reaction has finished.

State the expected colour of the pH paper when the reaction has finished, and explain why. **[2]**

....

....

....

....

4 Rock salt is a mixture of sodium chloride, which is soluble in water, and a number of insoluble solids, such as sand and clay.

Describe and explain the method you would use to obtain a sample of pure salt from rock salt. **[6]**

....

....

....

....

....

....

....

....

....

....

....

....

....

....

[Total = ... / 26 marks]

Further application

1 A student was planning an experiment to determine whether or not the yield of copper(II) sulfate obtained from this reaction was affected by the type of base used to neutralise the sulfuric acid.

The three bases they decided to use were copper(II) oxide, copper(II) carbonate, and copper(II) hydroxide.

a) Describe how the method described in **Required practical 1** could be changed to determine whether or not the type of base affects the overall yield of copper(II) sulfate.

You should include changes to make the comparison as fair as possible. **[3]**

....

....

....

....

....

....

....

....

b) Give the formula of copper(II) hydroxide. **[1]**

....

2 For the student's experiment:

a) identify the independent variable **[1]**

....

b) identify the dependent variable **[1]**

....

c) identify two control variables and a value for each one. **[2]**

Control 1: ....

Value: ....

Control 2: ....

Value: ....

d) The table below shows the student's results using 2.5 g of each base.
Complete the table.
You can assume that the maximum theoretical mass is 4.0 g. [3]

Base	Mass of copper(II) sulfate obtained / g			Mean mass of copper(II) sulfate	Percentage yield
	Repeat 1	Repeat 2	Repeat 3		
Copper(II) oxide	3.1	3.2	3.0		
Copper(II) carbonate	2.4	2.6	1.9		
Copper(II) hydroxide	2.9	3.2	2.9		

e) Write a brief conclusion for the student's experiment, using the results you have calculated. [3]

....

....

....

....

f) Use the concept of moles and limiting reagents to explain why the student's experiment is not valid for all of the bases that they tested. [6]

....

....

....

....

....

....

....

....

....

....

....

....

....

....

[Total = ... / 20 marks]

Chemistry

Required Practical 9: Investigating electrolysis of aqueous solutions

Electrolysis is an important process. It has many uses. These include extracting reactive metals, purifying copper, **electroplating** metal objects, and producing hydrogen gas, chlorine gas and sodium hydroxide from sea water. When **binary ionic compounds** are electrolysed in their molten state, they are split directly into their elements. However, when these same **compounds** are dissolved in water, the products of electrolysis can change depending on the different ions present.

Further information can be found in **AQA GCSE (9–1) Combined Science Student Book** on these pages:

- 218–223: Electrolysis
- 204–205: Oxidation and reduction in terms of electrons
- 203: Displacement reactions

Health and safety

- Wear eye protection.
- Tell your teacher about any spills, do not try to clean them up yourself.
- Hydrochloric acid solution is an irritant – you must wear eye protection. If it comes into contact with your eyes, wash them with running water for 5 minutes. Avoid getting the acid on your skin. Rinse affected area if this occurs.
- Chlorine is a respiratory irritant and is toxic at high levels. Use of low concentration solutions will limit the formation of chlorine gas. Only carry out the electrolysis for long enough to test the gas. Do not collect chlorine gas in a test tube. If possible, restrict electrolysis of chlorides to a fume cupboard.
- Use of electricity with aqueous solutions carries a risk of electrical shock. When setting up the electrolysis equipment, keep the electricity switched off at the socket until all equipment is fully set up and secure. Switch off the electricity at the socket while swapping over the solutions. Do not use a voltage higher than the voltage specified by your teacher.

Key terms

Binary ionic compound: a compound made up of ions of two different elements – one metal and one non-metal.

Compound: a substance made from two or more different elements chemically joined together.

Electrolysis: the decomposition of ionic compounds using electricity.

Electroplating: forming a layer of another metal onto a metal object using electrolysis.

Aim

Investigate what happens when **aqueous** *solutions are electrolysed using inert electrodes. This should be an investigation involving developing a* **hypothesis***.*

Maths opportunities

- Addition and subtraction
- Interpreting data from a table

Equipment and reagents

- Two graphite electrodes
- Two electrical wires
- Two crocodile clips
- 50 cm³ beaker
- White tile (optional)
- Access to water
- Blue litmus paper or Universal Indicator paper
- Tongs or tweezers
- Starch solution
- Scrubbing brush or sandpaper

- 0.1 mol/dm³ copper(II) nitrate solution
- 0.1 mol/dm³ hydrochloric acid solution
- 0.1 mol/dm³ sodium sulfate solution
- 0.1 mol/dm³ silver nitrate solution
- 0.1 mol/dm³ copper(II) chloride solution
- 0.1 mol/dm³ sodium iodide solution

Key terms

Aqueous: similar to water or dissolved in water.

Electrolyte: an ionic liquid or solution of aqueous ions that conducts electricity during electrolysis.

Hypothesis: a prediction or proposed explanation based on probable evidence.

Notes

- These solutions may be labelled A–F or by name; either way, it is important that you know the different solutions so that you can identify them during the practical.
- The equipment used to carry out the electrolysis may be different in your school depending on the resources you have available.

Hypothesis

For each **electrolyte**, give your predicted product and expected observations at the anode and cathode.

	Cathode (negative electrode)		Anode (positive electrode)	
	Observation (include physical state and test results for gases)	Identity of product	Observation (include physical state and test results for gases)	Identity of product
Copper(II) nitrate				
Hydrochloric acid				
Sodium sulfate				
Silver nitrate				
Copper(II) chloride				
Sodium iodide				

Method

Important: only carry out the electrolysis for long enough to test the gas.

1   Assemble the electrolysis circuit by connecting:
    - wires to a DC power pack
    - a crocodile clip to each wire
    - the graphite electrodes to the crocodile clips.
2   Add approximately 10 cm³ of the first solution to the beaker.
3   Dip the electrodes into the solution.
4   Turn the voltage on the power pack to the voltage specified by your teacher and switch on the electricity.
5   Observe the electrolysis and record what you see in the table in the **observations** section.
    Test any gas formed at the anode with damp blue litmus paper or Universal Indicator paper for the presence of chlorine gas. Hold the paper near the electrode and above the surface of the solution using tongs or tweezers. Do not dip the paper into the solution.
    Test any brown solution formed at the anode with starch solution.
6   Switch off the electricity.
7   Clean the electrodes with the scrubbing brush or sandpaper if a solid has formed on it, and rinse the beaker thoroughly with water.
8   Repeat steps 1–7 for the remaining solutions.

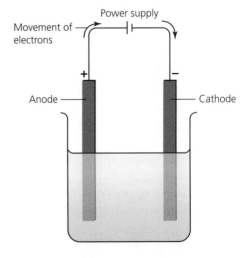

Note

If you have collected the gases in test tubes, you will also be able to test for the presence of hydrogen gas and oxygen gas. However, these gases should only be collected if the gases have tested negative for chlorine gas.

Observations

1 Use this table to record your results.

If the samples are not labelled A–F, use the same order of chemicals as in your hypothesis.

	Cathode (negative electrode)		Anode (positive electrode)	
	Observation (include physical state and test results for gases)	Identity of product	Observation (include physical state and test results for gases)	Identity of product
A				
B				
C				
D				
E				
F				

Conclusions

2 If applicable, by matching your results to your predicted results, identify the compounds in solutions A–F.

A: .... B: ....

C: .... D: ....

E: .... F: ....

3 Briefly describe the tests used for chlorine gas and iodine solution. Include the observation for positive results.

....

....

....

....

Tip

If you identified all of the compounds correctly, think about what you could do to provide more evidence for the identity of each electrolysis product.

....

....

....

....

....

....

....

....

....

....

Chemistry

Evaluation

4   If applicable, your teacher will tell you what the different solutions are.

Evaluate your experiment by comparing this with your results and hypothesis.

Be sure to include any improvements that could be made to increase your confidence in the results.

....

....

....

....

....

....

....

....

Chemistry

Exam-style questions

1   Brine is a solution of highly concentrated sodium chloride (NaCl). The electrolysis of brine is a useful industrial process, used to produce three separate products.

a) Predict the identities of the gases given off at both electrodes and a chemical test for each gas, including expected observations for a positive result.
Explain your answer in terms of the ions involved.   **[6]**

(HT)   You could also include ionic equations.

....

....

....

....

....

....

....

....

....

....

....

b) The third product of this reaction is an aqueous solution. When universal indicator is added to this product, it turns purple.

i) Complete and balance the equation for the reaction.   **[3]**

$2NaCl + 2H_2O \rightarrow$ .... $+ H_2 + Cl_2$

ii) Name the third product.   **[1]**

....

c) Graphite electrodes can be used to perform this electrolysis. Explain why graphite is a suitable material for this type of electrolysis.   **[2]**

....

....

(HT)   **d)** Write ionic equations for the processes occurring at the cathode.   **[2]**

....

....

....

Chemistry

2 It is possible to coat a metal object in silver metal using electrolysis. This is a form of electroplating.

a) To coat a metal object in silver, one of the electrodes must be replaced with the metal object; the silver will attach to the metal object instead of the electrode it has replaced.

Given that silver ions are Ag^+, identify which electrode must be replaced in this situation. **[1]**

....

b) The mass of silver deposited on a metal spoon was measured every 60 seconds during electroplating. The table shows the results.

Calculate the total mass of silver added to the spoon over 3 minutes. **[1]**

Time / s	0	60	120	180
Mass of spoon / g	22.4	22.8	23.2	23.6

....

....

....

....

c) Describe the trend in these results. **[2]**

....

....

....

(HT) **d)** What name is given to the process that forms silver atoms from silver ions at the cathode? **[1]**

....

(HT) **e)** Write an ionic equation for the process occurring at the anode. **[3]**

....

....

[Total = ... / 22 marks]

Further application

1 A student wanted to investigate the reactivity of metals.

They decided to put the metals in order of reactivity by observing the products made during the electrolysis of aqueous solutions containing four different metal ions.

The metal ions in the four solutions were magnesium, copper, silver and zinc.

a) By considering the products formed at the cathode during these electrolysis experiments, explain why this experiment is **not** suitable for putting the four metals in order of reactivity. [3]

....

....

....

....

....

....

b) Using your knowledge of displacement reactions and metal reactivity, describe a method that could be used to determine the order of reactivity for magnesium, copper, silver and zinc, including expected observations. [6]

> **Tip**
>
> You may give your expected observations in the form of a table using the space provided.

....

....

....

....

....

....

....

....

....

....

....

....

2 Electroplating can be used to coat common metals, such as iron, in a layer of gold to give the object a more pleasing appearance.

a) A student wanted to investigate the relationship between the current in an electrolysis experiment and the mass of gold deposited onto an object over a fixed period of time.

Identify the:

i) independent variable [1]

....

ii) dependent variable [1]

....

iii) two control variables. [2]

Control 1: ....

Control 2: ....

(HT) **b) i)** Balance this equation. [1]

$Au^{3+} + \ldots e^- \rightarrow Au$

ii) State the name of the process occurring in the equation. [1]

....

c) The compound used to release Au^{3+} ions into solution is gold chloride.
Give the formula of gold chloride. [1]

....

d) This table shows the mass of gold deposited onto a piece of iron over 2 minutes, and the current used in the electrolysis circuit.
Describe the trend in these results. [2]

Current / A	Mass of gold deposited / g
0.1	0.44
0.2	0.89
0.3	1.32
0.4	1.75

....

....

....

....

....

e) Predict the mass of gold added over 2 minutes using a current of 0.6 A. [1]

....

....

[Total = ... / 19 marks]

Required practical 10: Investigating the variables that affect temperature changes in reacting solutions

Exothermic reactions are reactions that release heat energy into the surroundings. This energy release is often the reason for performing the reactions – during cooking or generating electrical energy with steam, for example. There are numerous factors that affect how much energy is released during a reaction. This practical investigates how changing the mass of the reactants affects the change in temperature.

Health and safety

- Wear eye protection.
- Tell your teacher about any spills, do not try to clean them up yourself.
- Hydrochloric acid solution is an irritant – you must wear eye protection and avoid getting the acid (hot or cold) on your skin. Rinse hands if this occurs.
- Magnesium powder is flammable and an irritant. Keep the magnesium away from sources of flame.
- Hydrogen gas is flammable. Keep the gas produced by the reaction away from sources of flame and perform the experiment in a well-ventilated area.

Aim

Investigate the variables that affect temperature changes in reacting solutions such as: acid plus metals; acid plus carbonates; neutralisations; displacement of metals.

Note

In this practical we are looking at a **neutralisation** reaction of a metal with an acid, but it covers the techniques involved when measuring heat release by any experiment that causes a water-based solution to heat up.

Equipment and reagents

- 250 cm³ beaker
- 25 cm³ measuring cylinder
- Expanded polystyrene cup
- Thermometer (ideally measuring from −10 °C to 100 °C)
- Weighing boat
- Spatula
- Mass balance (ideally measuring to 2 decimal places)
- 1.0 mol/dm³ hydrochloric acid solution
- Magnesium powder

Method

1 Place the expanded polystyrene cup into the beaker to keep it stable.
2 Use a measuring cylinder to measure out 25 cm³ of hydrochloric acid solution. Pour this into the polystyrene cup.
3 Place the thermometer into the acid.
4 Use a mass balance to carefully weigh out 0.1 g of magnesium powder into a weighing boat.
5 Record the starting temperature of the solution.
6 Add the magnesium to the solution quickly. Stir the mixture carefully with the thermometer.
7 Check the temperature regularly until the temperature stops rising. Record the maximum temperature reached in the **observations** section.
8 Clean out the polystyrene cup and repeat steps 1–7 for a second set of results.
9 Clean out the polystyrene cup and repeat steps 1–8, using up to four different masses of magnesium (0.2 g, 0.3 g, 0.4 g and 0.5 g).

Note

There are a number of alternative reactions that can be used in this experiment. The masses and volumes and use will change for different reactions and your teacher will provide you with alternative quantities.

Further information can be found in **AQA GCSE (9–1) Combined Science Student Book** on these pages:

231–232: Exothermic and endothermic reactions

176–198: Quantitative chemistry

202: Reaction with dilute acids

Maths opportunities

- Addition and subtraction
- Calculating mean values
- Plotting and interpreting graphs
- Calculating moles from mass and from concentration
- Measuring volumes, masses and temperatures

Key terms

Endothermic reaction: a reaction that absorbs heat energy (and so causes a decrease in temperature).

Exothermic reaction: a reaction that releases heat energy (and so causes an increase in temperature).

Neutralisation: the reaction between an acid and an alkali, base, carbonate or metal that produces a salt with a pH of 7.

Tip

If you are using a long thermometer, use a clamp and stand to ensure the thermometer is secure.

Observations

1   Record the temperature changes that you observe during the reaction between your chosen reagents (magnesium and hydrochloric acid, for example).

Mass / g	Repeat 1			Repeat 2			Mean temperature rise / °C
	Starting temperature / °C	Maximum temperature / °C	Temperature rise / °C	Starting temperature / °C	Maximum temperature / °C	Temperature rise / °C	

Conclusions

2   a) Plot a graph of your results.

b) Describe the trend in your results.

....

....

....

....

(HT) **3** Explain the trend shown in your results in terms of limiting reagents.

Tip 💡
You can choose to use moles calculations in your answer to support your explanation.

....

....

....

....

....

....

....

....

Evaluation

4 The theoretical maximum temperature rise is 55.5°C for this specific reaction.

Compare this with the result that you obtained, and evaluate the experiment.

Suggest any improvements that could be made to the experiment based on your evaluation.

....

....

....

....

....

....

....

....

Exam-style questions

1   25 cm³ of 1.0 mol/dm³ sodium hydroxide reacts with 25 cm³ of 1.0 mol/dm³ hydrochloric acid in a neutralisation reaction.

The temperature of the reaction changed from 21°C to 29°C.

a) Identify whether this reaction is exothermic or **endothermic**.   [1]

....

b) Draw a reaction profile for this type of reaction. Include labelled arrows to show:
   - reactants
   - products
   - activation energy
   - overall energy change.   [4]

Energy

Progress of reaction

c) Calculate the temperature rise during the reaction.   [1]

....

d) Explaining your answer in both cases, predict what the temperature rise would be if:

   i)   the concentration of **one** of the reactants was doubled   [2]

....

....

....

   ii) the concentration of **both** of the reactants was doubled.   [2]

....

....

....

Chemistry

2 **a)** The neutralisation of sulfuric acid with calcium carbonate is a reaction used to neutralise acidic soil.
    The products of this reaction are calcium sulfate, carbon dioxide and water.
    Write the symbol equation for this reaction. [1]

    ....

    In a laboratory test, 50 cm³ of 1.0 mol/dm³ was added to different masses of calcium carbonate. The results are shown in this table.

Mass of calcium carbonate / g	Starting temperature / °C	Final temperature / °C	Temperature rise / °C
1	22	24	
2	21	25	
3	22	28	
4	21	29	
5	21	31	
6	21	31	

    b) Complete the table. [2]

    c) Describe and explain the trend in the results. [2]

    ....

    ....

    ....

(HT) **d)** Explain, in terms of the moles of acid and the moles of calcium carbonate, why this reaction reaches its maximum temperature rise at 5 g. [3]

    ....

    ....

    ....

    e) Use the following equation to calculate the heat energy released when 5 g of calcium carbonate reacts with the sulfuric acid.
    Assume 1 cm³ of the acid weighs 1 g. [2]
    heat energy (J) = mass of acid (g) × 4.2 × temperature rise (°C)

    ....

    ....

    ....

    [Total = ... / 20 marks]

Further application

1 A group of students wanted to see if they could determine the order of reactivity of different metals.

They planned to measure the change in temperature when reacting different metals with a solution of copper(II) sulfate.

The metals they wanted to test were iron, zinc and magnesium.

a) Write a method that the students could use to determine the heat released during these reactions.

You should include:
- a brief method
- independent, dependent and control variables
- an explanation of how the test will be made fair. **[6]**

....

....

....

....

....

....

....

....

....

....

....

....

....

....

....

b) Each metal is added to 50 cm³ of highly concentrated copper(II) sulfate. The temperature rise per gram of metal is shown in this table.

Metal	Temperature rise per gram / °C/g
Zinc	18
Iron	7
Magnesium	35

Using the formula below, calculate the energy released by 1 g of each metal.
Assume 1 cm³ of copper sulfate has a mass of 1 g. **[3]**

heat energy (J) = mass of acid (g) × 4.2 × temperature rise (°C)

....

....

....

....

c) Based on this set of results, put the metals in order of reactivity. Give your reasons. **[2]**

....

....

....

(HT)

d) Using your knowledge of the relationship between mass, moles and M_r, calculate the energy released by one mole of each metal. **[3]**

....

....

....

....

....

....

[Total = ... / 14 marks]

Required practical 11: Investigating how changes in concentration affect the rates of reactions

Controlling the rate of a reaction is particularly important for industrial chemists who want to make their product as quickly and efficiently as possible. Even in everyday life we try to control the rate of reactions – chilling food to slow the rate at which it goes off, or using chemicals to quickly clean kitchen surfaces, for example. One of the simplest ways to change the rate of reaction is to change the concentration of a solution.

Aim

Investigate the effect of concentration on the rate of a reaction involving measuring the volume of gas and a reaction involving a colour change or **turbidity***. This investigation includes the development of a hypothesis.*

Hypothesis

Both reactions involve increasing the concentration of hydrochloric acid from $0.1\,mol/dm^3$ up to $2.0\,mol/dm^3$, with all other factors being kept the same. Predict what will happen to the rate of reaction as the concentration of the acid increases. How will this be shown in both experiments? Explain your reasons with relation to collision theory.

> **Note**
>
> Refer to page 478 of **AQA GCSE (9– 1) Combined Science Student Book** (*or CS 2: 122*) for more information about collision theory.

> **Tip**
>
> If you want to relate your hypothesis specifically to the reactions you will be doing, you will first need to read the methods you will be using.

....
....
....
....
....
....
....
....

Part A: Measuring the volume of a gas produced

Equipment and reagents

- $25\,cm^3$ measuring cylinder
- $50\,cm^3$ measuring cylinder
- $100\,cm^3$ conical flask (or suitable alternative)
- Water trough
- Bung with attached delivery tube
- Weighing boat
- Stopwatch

- Mass balance (ideally measuring to 2 decimal places)
- Access to water
- Hydrochloric acid solution of concentrations $0.1\,mol/dm^3$, $0.5\,mol/dm^3$, $1.0\,mol/dm^3$, $1.5\,mol/dm^3$, $2.0\,mol/dm^3$
- Small marble chips

Method

1 Use the $25\,cm^3$ measuring cylinder to measure $20\,cm^3$ of hydrochloric acid solution. Pour it into the conical flask.

Further information can be found in AQA GCSE (9–1) Combined Science Student Book on these pages:
- 478–485: Factors affecting the rate of reactions (or *CS 2: 122–129*)
- 176–198: Quantitative chemistry

Key terms

Hypothesis: a prediction or proposed explanation based on probable evidence.
Turbidity: the cloudiness of a solution.

Key equations $\quad x+y=z$

Gas volume:
$$rate\,(cm^3/s) = \frac{volume\,of\,gas\,(cm^3)}{time\,taken\,(s)}$$

$$Turbidity:rate = \frac{1}{reaction\,time}$$

Health and safety

- Wear eye protection.
- Tell your teacher about any spills, do not try to clean them up yourself.
- Hydrochloric acid solution is an irritant – you must wear eye protection and avoid getting the acid on your skin. Rinse affected area if this occurs.
- Calcium carbonate (in the form of marble chips) is a low hazard chemical.
- Sodium thiosulfate is classed as a low hazard chemical.

Maths opportunities $\quad \sqrt{2^3+1}$

- Rounding to an appropriate number of decimal places or significant figures
- Addition and subtraction
- Calculating mean values
- Calculating rate
- Plotting and interpreting a graph, including determining the gradient
- Calculating moles from concentration
- Measuring volumes and times

2 Use the mass balance to measure out 1.00 g of small marble chips into the weighing boat.
3 Fill the water trough with water up to a depth of approximately 5 cm.
4 Fill the 50 cm³ measuring cylinder with water.
5 Place your flat palm on top of the 50 cm³ measuring cylinder. Turn the cylinder upside down and place the bottom of the measuring cylinder below the surface of the water in the trough. The water in the cylinder should stay where it is.
6 Put the end of the delivery tube under the end of the 50 cm³ measuring cylinder.
7 The following should be done as soon as possible, one after the other: add the marble chips to the acid, put the bung into the top of the conical flask, and start the stopwatch.
8 Time the reaction for 60 seconds. Record the volume of gas released in that time. If the volume of gas reaches 50 cm³ before 60 seconds has passed, record the time it has taken for the volume to reach 50 cm³.

Note

The water should be up to the very top of the measuring cylinder.

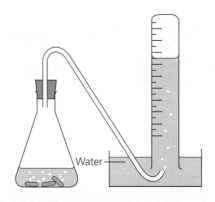

Water

Tip

Make sure you record your results immediately after each experiment so that you do not lose track of the type of result you are recording for step 8.

9 Repeat steps 1–8 for the remaining concentrations of hydrochloric acid.

Part B: Observing turbidity of a solution

Equipment and reagents

- 5 cm³ measuring cylinder
- 10 cm³ measuring cylinder
- Sample vial
- Stopwatch
- Paper with black cross on it

- Hydrochloric acid solution of concentrations: 0.1 mol/dm³, 0.5 mol/dm³, 1.0 mol/dm³, 1.5 mol/dm³, and 2.0 mol/dm³
- 0.2 mol/dm³ sodium thiosulfate solution

Tip

As the reaction proceeds, you should swirl the reaction mixture consistently until the reaction has finished. Alternatively, do not swirl the reaction at all. Whichever you choose to do, be consistent.

Health and safety ⚠

- Wear eye protection.
- Tell your teacher about any spills, do not try to clean them up yourself.
- Hydrochloric acid solution is an irritant – you must wear eye protection and avoid getting the acid on your skin. Rinse affected area if this occurs.
- Sulfur dioxide is produced in small quantities during this reaction. Ensure the reaction is performed in a well-ventilated area. If you have respiratory difficulties (such as asthma) you must have ready access to any treatment and be able to remove yourself from the laboratory if needed.
- Sodium thiosulfate is classed as a low hazard chemical.

Note

A low hazard chemical is a chemical that does not pose an immediate risk to human health in cases of low level exposure. However, general laboratory safety rules should still be applied in cases of spillage and exposure to the skin or eyes.

Method

1 Use the 10 cm³ measuring cylinder to measure 6 cm³ of sodium thiosulfate solution. Pour it into the sample vial.
2 Use the 5 cm³ measuring cylinder to measure out 2 cm³ of 0.1 mol/dm³ hydrochloric acid.
3 Place the sample vial on top of the black cross.
4 Quickly add the acid to the sample vial, swirl the solution and, at the same time, start the stopwatch.
5 Look at the black cross through the solution in the sample vial. A yellow precipitate will form and start to obscure the cross.
6 Stop the stopwatch as soon as you can no longer see the black cross.
7 Repeat steps 1–6 twice more for a total of three repeat readings for this concentration.
8 Repeat steps 1–7 for the remaining concentrations of hydrochloric acid.

Tips

- You could use syringes instead of measuring cylinders.
- The cross could be drawn on the bottom of the vial using a permanent marker pen.

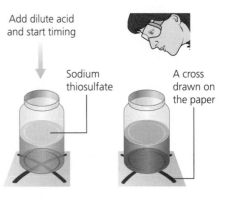

Add dilute acid and start timing

Sodium thiosulfate

A cross drawn on the paper

Observations

1 Complete these tables for parts A and B. Remember that:

$$\text{rate (cm}^3\text{ s}^{-1}) = \frac{\text{volume of gas (cm}^3)}{\text{time taken (s)}}$$

Part A

Concentration of hydrochloric acid / mol/dm³	Volume of gas after 60 s / cm³ OR Time taken to make 50 cm³ of gas / s	Rate of reaction / cm³/s
0.1		
0.5		
1.0		
1.5		
2.0		

Part B

| Concentration of hydrochloric acid / mol/dm³ | Time taken for cross to disappear in s | | | Mean time / s | Rate of reaction |
	Repeat 1	Repeat 2	Repeat 3		
0.1					
0.5					
1.0					
1.5					
2.0					

Conclusions

2 Using your results from both experiments, describe the general trend shown.

....

....

....

....

....

....

....

....

....

....

....

....

....

....

3 Plot *rate of reaction* against *concentration of hydrochloric acid* on this grid.

Tip 💡

It is possible to plot both graphs on the same grid by using two *y*-axes – one on the left and one on the right. Alternatively you could use a second grid and plot two separate graphs.

Tip 💡

m is equivalent to the gradient of the graph. It is calculated by dividing the change in the *y* value by the change in the *x* value.

c is the *y*-intercept. It can be found where the straight line meets the *y*-axis.

(HT) 4 Both graphs should give straight lines of best fit. Use your graph to express the equation of each line in the form $y = mx + c$.

....

....

....

....

....

....

Evaluation

5 The relationship between the rate of reaction and the concentration of a reactant solution should be directly proportional (the graph should be a straight line starting at (0, 0)).

Evaluate your experiment by comparing this ideal to the set of results you obtained for both experiments.

....

....

....

....

....

....

....

Chemistry

Exam-style questions

1 a) Balance the reaction between magnesium metal and nitric acid. [1]

   $\ldots\ldots Mg_{(s)} + \ldots\ldots HNO_{3(aq)} \rightarrow \ldots\ldots Mg(NO_3)_{2(aq)} + \ldots\ldots H_{2(g)}$

   b) State two methods that could be used to determine the rate of this reaction by referring to the physical states of the products. Explain why you have chosen these methods. [3]

   ....

   ....

   ....

   ....

   ....

   c) Explain, in terms of particles, two ways in which the rate of this reaction could be increased by changing factors relating to the nitric acid only. [6]

   ....

   ....

   ....

   ....

   ....

   ....

   ....

   ....

2 Ammonia and hydrogen chloride are both gases. They react together to form a white solid, ammonium chloride.

   $NH_{3(g)} + HCl_{(g)} \rightarrow NH_4Cl_{(g)}$

   The time taken to form 10 g of ammonium chloride was recorded at different pressures of gas. The results are shown in this table.

Pressure of gas / Pa	Time taken to form 10 g of ammonium chloride / s	Rate of reaction / g/s
100 000	44.4	
200 000	22.1	
300 000	14.8	
400 000	11.0	
500 000	8.9	
600 000	7.4	

   a) Complete the table by calculating the rates of reaction. [2]

   b) Describe the relationship between the pressure of gas and the rate of reaction. [3]

   ....

3 a) This graph shows the volume of gas produced during the reaction between hydrochloric acid and zinc to produce zinc chloride and hydrogen gas.

Two concentrations of acid were used; both are shown.

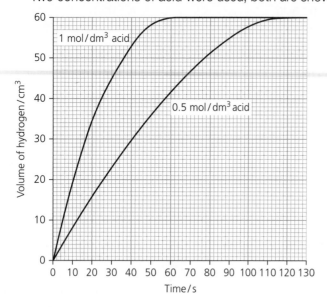

Using the graph, identify the time at which the reaction stops when using 1.0 mol/dm³ hydrochloric acid. **[1]**

....

b) Calculate the rate of reaction at the beginning of the reaction for each concentration. **[4]**

....

....

....

....

....

c) Explain why the rate of reaction slows down as the reaction proceeds. **[2]**

....

....

....

d) Which of these reactants is likely to be in excess? Explain your answer. **[2]**

....

....

....

[Total = ... / 24 marks]

Chemistry

Further application

1 A student wanted to investigate the efficiency of four different catalysts on the decomposition of hydrogen peroxide. The balanced symbol equation for the reaction is:

$$2H_2O_2 \rightarrow 2H_2O + O_2$$

The catalysts they wanted to test were: iron(III) oxide; lead(IV) oxide; and manganese(IV) oxide.

The student also tested the reaction without a catalyst, as a control experiment.

a) The student added 0.2 g of each catalyst to a mixture of 25 cm³ of 3% hydrogen peroxide solution and two drops of washing up liquid.

They measured the height of the foam that was formed after 30 seconds.

Using this diagram, state and explain the order of effectiveness for these catalysts. **[2]**

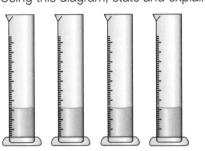
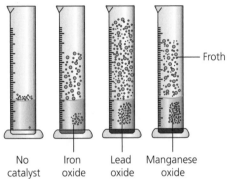

Measuring cylinders containing
25 cm³ hydrogen peroxide solution
+ 2 drops of washing-up liquid

No catalyst Iron oxide Lead oxide Manganese oxide

— Froth

after 30 seconds

> **Note**
>
> See pages 480–481 of **AQA GCSE (9–1) Combined Science Student Book** (*or CS 2: 124–125*) for more information on catalysts.

....

....

....

....

....

....

....

....

b) At the end of the reaction, the reaction can be filtered and the solid catalysts can be washed and dried.
What mass of iron(III) oxide would you expect to recover? Explain your answer. **[2]**

....

....

....

c) Discuss the limitations of this experiment. **[2]**

....

....

....

....

....

2 The precipitation of sulfur from the reaction of sodium thiosulfate can be monitored using a light sensor. A light is shone through the reaction mixture and, as the sulfur precipitate forms, the light intensity reaching the sensor decreases.

5 cm³ of 1.0 mol/dm³ hydrochloric acid was added to 10 cm³ of 0.2 mol/dm³ of sodium thiosulfate solution at four different temperatures.

All other factors were kept the same. The results of this experiment are shown below:

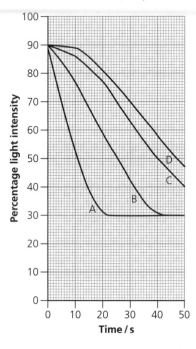

a) Give the letter (A, B, C or D) of the curve that represents the reaction with the lowest reaction temperature. Explain your choice. **[2]**

....

....

....

b) The reaction is considered to be complete at 30% light intensity. Calculate the mean rate of reaction for experiment B. **[2]**

....

....

....

c) Explain the results of this experiment using particle theory. **[2]**

....

....

....

....

....

d) Balance the following equation for the reaction of sodium thiosulfate with hydrochloric acid. **[1]**

..... $Na_2S_2O_3$ + ... HCl → ..... S + ... SO_2 + ... $NaCl$ + ... H_2O

[Total = ... / 13 marks]

Required practical 12: Investigating paper chromatography

Chromatography is a technique used to separate a mixture of liquid or aqueous chemicals. It works because different chemicals travel at different speeds during the technique, depending on how soluble they are in the solvent (known as the **mobile phase**) that travels up the paper (known as the **stationary phase**). This technique can be used to purify chemicals, but its most common use at GCSE is as an analytical technique for identifying the presence of different coloured chemicals in a mixture.

Aim

Use paper chromatography to separate and tell the difference between coloured substances, including the calculation of **R_f values**.

Equipment and reagents

- 25 cm³ beaker
- Piece of chromatography paper
- Glass rod
- Pencil
- Ruler
- Felt tip pens (at least two, but up to four or six, depending on the width of your chromatography paper)
- Access to water

Method

1 Add water to the beaker, to a depth of 1 cm.
2 Draw a line, in pencil, 2 cm from the bottom edge of the chromatography paper. This is the start line.
3 Choose two, four or six different-coloured felt tip pens (depending on the width of the chromatography paper). Place a small dot of each pen, equally spaced, along the start line.
4 Fold or wrap the top edge of the chromatography paper over a glass rod.
5 Place the chromatography paper into the water with the glass rod laid across the beaker to keep the paper upright. The water level must be below the start line.

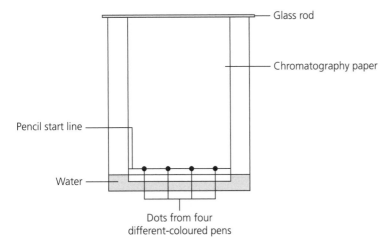

Glass rod

Chromatography paper

Pencil start line

Water

Dots from four different-coloured pens

6 When the water level is approximately 1 cm from the top of the paper, remove the paper from the water and mark the position the water reached with a pencil. Leave it somewhere safe to dry.

Further information can be found in **AQA GCSE (9–1) Combined Science Student Book** on these pages:

- 510–515: Purity, formulations and chromatography (*or CS 2: 154–159*)

Key terms

Aqueous: similar to water or dissolved in water.

Mobile phase: the liquid or gas that flows through a chromatography system, moving the materials to be separated over the stationary phase.

R_f value: the ratio of the distance moved by a substance to the distance moved by the solvent during chromatography.

Stationary phase: the solid or liquid phase of a chromatography system which causes the materials to be separated to move at different rates.

Health and safety

- Tell your teacher about any spills, do not try to clean them up yourself.
- All chemicals involved in this experiment are deemed to be low risk. However, standard laboratory safety rules still apply at all times.

Maths opportunities

- Measuring distances
- Calculating ratios

Key equation

$$R_f = \frac{\text{distance travelled by component}}{\text{distance travelled by solvent}}$$

Tip

There are multiple ways of supporting the paper during chromatography, such as:

- using a wooden splint and paperclip
- folding the paper parallel to the long edge so the paper can support itself
- piercing the paper at the top with a long wire or rod
- putting the paper into a conical flask and trapping the paper using a bung
- using a thin piece of chromatography paper in a boiling tube.

Observations

1 Describe what you observe when the chromatography is complete.

For future revision, it may be useful to staple your chromatogram into this book, or take a photo.

$$R_f = \frac{\text{distance travelled by component}}{\text{distance travelled by solvent}}$$

> **Tip**
>
> When calculating the R_f value, measure the distance between the pencil line and the front of the component all the time to make sure the results are consistent.

> **Tip**
>
> When describing chromatography experiments, the key observations include
> - how many different components (spots of pigment) each ink splits up into
> - the R_f value of each component
> - whether or not any of the inks contained the same components.

....

....

....

....

....

....

....

....

....

....

....

....

....

Conclusions

2 The greater the R_f value of a component, the more soluble it is in water.

Describe the component that is most soluble in water and the component that is least soluble in water. Refer to the colour and the R_f values to support your answer.

....

....

....

....

....

Evaluation

3 The spots on your chromatograph should be well separated, and the components of each ink should not have mixed with each other.

Use this information to evaluate your own chromatograph, including any improvements that could be made to improve its quality.

....

....

....

....

....

....

....

....

You may want to attach your chromatography paper here for your records.

Exam-style questions

1 A student was investigating the composition of six different inks.

They carried out a simple paper chromatography experiment with the different inks labelled A–F.

This is their chromatogram:

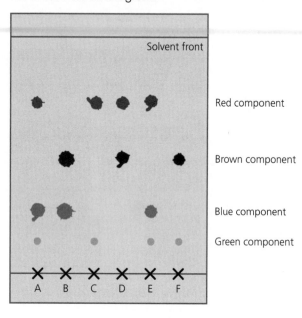

a) Identify how many different substances were present in the six inks. **[1]**

....

b) Identify whether any of the inks were pure. Explain your answer. **[2]**

....

....

c) State and explain which of the two inks are identical. **[2]**

....

....

d) Identify which is the most soluble substance in this chromatogram. Explain your answer. **[2]**

....

....

e) Calculate the R_f value of the least soluble component, using a ruler. Show your workings. **[2]**

....

....

Chemistry

2 a) One use of chromatography is to test the purity of medicinal chemicals.

A scientist wanted to test a sample of aspirin that they made in the laboratory. The scientist performed chromatography under a near-UV 'blacklight', which makes the different components glow blue.

State how many components you would expect to see if the sample was pure. **[1]**

....

....

b) When testing the aspirin sample, the most intensely coloured component had travelled 3 cm. The solvent had travelled 8 cm.

Calculate the R_f value of this component. **[1]**

....

....

c) A second, less intensely coloured component, was detected. Its R_f value was calculated as 0.875.

Calculate the distance travelled by this component. Show your workings. **[2]**

....

....

....

d) The scientist carried out another test using the same batch of aspirin and the same solvent. In the resulting chromatograph, the component from part c) travelled 10.5 cm.

Calculate the distance travelled by the solvent in this chromatogram. Show your workings. **[3]**

....

....

....

....

e) The scientist discovered that the less intensely coloured component was salicylic acid, one of the starting materials for making aspirin.

The reaction started with 80 g of salicylic acid. There was 16 g of salicylic acid left unreacted at the end of the reaction.

Calculate the percentage of salicylic acid that reacted. **[3]**

....

....

....

....

[Total = ... / 19 marks]

Further application

1   Gas chromatography is a more advanced technique used to analyse small quantities of chemical mixtures. This is a simple summary of the method:

A   A sample is injected into the gas chromatograph.
B   The sample is vaporised.
C   The sample is pushed through a long, thin metal tube coated, on the inside, with a layer of solid silicone polymer by a stream of inert nitrogen gas.

D   Components that are attracted to the silicone polymers are 'held back' and so take longer to travel through the tube and reach the detector.
E   The time taken for the sample to travel through the tube to the detector is known as the retention time.

a) From the above description, identify:

   i)   the mobile phase .... [1]

   ii) the stationary phase. .... [1]

b) Why must the tube in the gas chromatograph be very long?   [1]

....

....

c) Gas chromatography–mass spectrometry (GC–MS) is a technique that combines gas chromatography's ability to separate mixtures, with mass spectrometry's ability to show the relative molecular mass of each component. GC–MS is used by the police and anti-doping agencies to test blood samples of suspected drunk drivers and drug cheats.
    Explain why paper chromatography is unsuitable for this use.   [1]

....

....

....

d) Compare and contrast gas chromatography and paper chromatography.
    Include their similarities and differences, and the advantages of each.   [6]

....

....

....

....

....

....

....

....

....

....

....

....

[Total = ... / 10 marks]

Chemistry

Required practical 13: Analysing and purifying water samples

When water is extracted from natural sources, it is not pure. It contains a number of different **solutes**, from dissolved gases to dissolved minerals. Water in temperate countries, such as the UK, has a low concentration of these solutes. However, in places with low rainfall, such as the Middle East, the only readily available source of water is seawater. Seawater has a high concentration of solutes, mostly dissolved salt. It is unsafe to drink.

Producing **potable water** from seawater is called **desalination**. It is an expensive process because lots of energy is required to generate heat or pressure. The simplest method of desalination is **distillation**.

Aim

Purify and analyse water samples from different sources, including pH, dissolved solids and distillation.

Equipment and reagents

- 10 cm³ measuring cylinder
- 100 cm³ conical flask
- Delivery tube with bung
- 100 cm³ beaker
- Boiling tube
- Bunsen burner, tripod, gauze and heatproof mat
- Wire loop
- Marker pen
- Mass balance
- Test tubes
- Dropping pipettes

- Seawater
- Access to water
- Ice
- Samples of impure water, labelled A–C
- 0.4 mol/dm³ sodium hydroxide solution
- 0.1 mol/dm³ barium chloride solution
- 0.1 mol/dm³ nitric acid solution
- 0.1 mol/dm³ silver nitrate solution
- Universal indicator

Health and safety

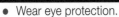

- Wear eye protection.
- Tell your teacher about any spills, do not try to clean them up yourself.
- Barium chloride solution is harmful. You must wear eye protection at all times until the experiment is put away. Wash affected areas immediately upon contact with skin. Wash your hands thoroughly at the end of the experiment.
- Hydrochloric acid solution, nitric acid solution, sodium hydroxide solution and silver nitrate solution are all irritants – you must wear eye protection and avoid getting the acid on your skin. Rinse affected area if this occurs.
- Bunsen burners and hot wire loops can cause serious burns. Allow equipment to cool on a heatproof mat before touching. If a burn occurs, hold the affected area under cold running water for at least 10 minutes.
- Treat all unknown solutions as harmful. If solutions come into contact with the skin, wash the affected area immediately.
- Do not continue to heat the mixture once all the water has been distilled off.

Further information can be found in **AQA GCSE (9–1) Combined Science Student Book** on these pages:

- 137–140: Separating mixtures
- 551–553: Producing potable water (*or CS 2: 195–197*)
- 214: Reaction of acids with metal carbonates

Key terms

Desalination: removal of dissolved solids from seawater.

Distillation: the separation of a specific liquid (usually the solvent) from a solution.

Potable water: water that is safe to drink.

Purification: the separation of a mixture into separate elements or compounds.

Solvent: a liquid that dissolves a solid or gas to form a solution.

Solute: a gas or solid that is dissolved in a solvent, such as water, to form a solution.

Maths opportunities

- Addition and subtraction
- Measuring masses
- Calculating mean averages
- Calculating molar quantities
- Ratios
- Decimal places and significant figures

Method

In this practical you will test samples of water, including seawater, distilled water, and unknown water samples, labelled A–C. You may be asked to identify the compounds in the unknown water samples by completing five chemical tests. It is important to perform these tests in the order that they are given so that specific compounds can be eliminated at specific points.

Part A: Purification of seawater

1 Use the mass balance to weigh the conical flask. Record its mass in the **observations** section.
2 Use the measuring cylinder to measure 10 cm³ of seawater. Pour this into the conical flask.
3 Put some ice into the beaker.
4 Connect the conical flask to the distillation apparatus as shown in the diagram. Ensure all the glassware is securely set up before beginning the next step.

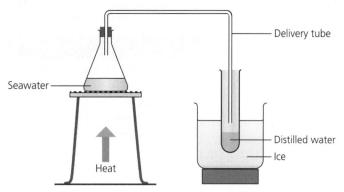

Delivery tube

Seawater

Distilled water

Ice

Heat

Note

If you have the appropriate equipment, you may use a quick-fit round bottom flask with a Liebig condenser. Check with your teacher or technician for help using this apparatus.

5 Light the Bunsen burner. Heat the reaction mixture gently using a blue flame with the airhole slightly open.
6 Allow the distillation to proceed until all the water has been distilled from the conical flask.
7 Turn off the Bunsen burner. Remove the delivery tube from the boiling tube. Allow the conical flask to cool. You will need the conical flask and salt for a later step.

Tip

Using the Bunsen burner with the air hole slightly open will produce a cooler flame, reducing the risk of the seawater boiling suddenly and bubbling into the glass tube.

Tip

Ensure that the delivery tube is not in the distilled water when the Bunsen burner is turned off. If the steam starts to cool while the delivery tube is in the distilled water, it can cause the distilled water to be 'sucked back' into the conical flask with the seawater in it.

Tip

Be very careful during step 7 as the glassware may be hot.

Part B: Testing water samples

1 Use chemical tests to test the seawater, the distilled water (from **Part A**), and the unknown water samples A–C.
Use the chemical tests in this order:
- pH test with universal indicator
- flame test
- sodium hydroxide test
- sulfate test
- halide test

2 Write down your findings in the **observations** section. Use your results to identify the compounds in water samples A–C.
3 Weigh the conical flask from **Part A**, which should now have cooled and will contain the left-over salt. Record the mass in the **observations** section. Use your results to calculate the mass of salt dissolved in the sample of seawater.

Tip

The chemical tests are explained on the next page.

Note

You should collect a fresh sample of seawater to perform the tests.

Test 1: pH test

1   Add $\frac{1}{3}$ of a spatula of each solid sample to separate test tubes. Label each tube appropriately.
2   Dissolve each of the samples in 2–3 cm³ deionised water.
3   Add 3–5 drops of universal indicator to the first test tube. Record your observations.
4   Repeat step 3 for the remaining samples.

Test 2: Flame test

1   Add approximately 10 cm³ of water to the beaker.
2   Set up the Bunsen burner on the heatproof mat.
3   Dip a wooden splint into water, then into one of your solid samples.
4   Put the splint and sample just above the bright blue cone of a roaring blue Bunsen flame. Record the colour given off by the ions in the flame.
5   Repeat steps 3–5 using the remaining solid samples and a fresh splint each time.

Tip

A roaring blue flame is the flame created when the air hole of a Bunsen burner is fully open; it gets its name from the sound it makes.

Tip

Make sure the air hole of the Bunsen burner is fully open to get the clearest colour during the flame test.

Test 3: Sodium hydroxide test

1   Add a spatula of each solid sample to separate test tubes. Label each tube appropriately.
2   Dissolve each sample in 2–3 cm³ of deionised water. If the solid does not dissolve in water, use nitric acid.
3   Use a pipette to add a few drops of sodium hydroxide solution to each sample. Record your observations.
4   If a white precipitate forms when a few drops are used, add an excess of sodium hydroxide and record any observations.

Note

Dissolving the solid in a minimum amount of water means adding small volumes of water until all of the solid has dissolved. The same technique is used when adding nitric acid to the insoluble compounds. You may see fizzing when adding the nitric acid.

Tip

An excess means a quantity larger than the minimum amount needed for the reaction to happen. The exact volume required for an excess of sodium hydroxide depends on the quantities of the solid sample and the deionised water that you have used. You should not need to add any more than 5 cm³ (approximately five full pipettes).

Test 4: Test for sulfates

1   Add $\frac{1}{3}$ of a spatula of each solid sample to separate test tubes. Label each tube appropriately.
2   Dissolve each sample in 2–3 cm³ of deionised water.
3   Add one pipette full of barium chloride solution to each sample. Record your observations.
4   Any samples that form a white precipitate should not be used in the remaining test as they can now be positively identified as metal sulfates.

Test 5: Test for halides

1   Add $\frac{1}{3}$ of a spatula of each solid sample to separate test tubes. Label each tube appropriately.
2   Dissolve each sample in 2–3 cm³ of deionised water.
3   Add one pipette full of nitric acid solution to each sample.
4   Add one pipette full of silver nitrate solution to each sample. Record your observations.

Note

Halide ions that react with silver nitrate produce a precipitate; its colour depends on the halide – white precipitate for chloride, cream (pale yellow) precipitate for bromide, and yellow precipitate for iodide.

It can be difficult to tell the difference between the positive result for bromide and iodide using this test – unless you see them side-by-side. Iodide gives a more yellow precipitate than bromide. Your teacher may show you the colour of each precipitate so you can compare.

Observations

1 Use this table to calculate the mass of dissolved solid in the sea water.

Mass of conical flask / g	Mass of conical flask + salt / g	Mass of salt in 10 cm³ of seawater / g

Tip

Describe what you see as thoroughly as possible. If a change occurs, describe the appearance before and after (for example, change from clear colourless solution to cream precipitate).

2 Record your observations for the chemical tests in this table.

Sample	pH Test	Flame test	Sodium hydroxide test	Sulfate test	Halide test
Seawater					
Distilled water					
A					
B					
C					

Conclusions

3 a) Name the main compound present in seawater.

....

b) Explain the test results for distilled water in terms of any ions present.

....

....

....

4 Use the test results to identify compounds A–C.
Give brief explanations of what each test tells you about the ions in each of the compounds.

A: ....

....

....

B: ....

....

....

C: ....

....

....

Evaluation

5   Your teacher will give you expected observations for each of the five water samples, as well as the identities of the compounds in the seawater sample and water samples A–C.

Did you identify each compound correctly?

If not, briefly explain your mistake(s) and how you could avoid it in future tests.

Tip

If you got one or more of the compounds wrong, work out what you *should* have observed for each one. Compare the expected results with your observations to help determine what may have gone wrong.

....

....

....

....

....

....

....

....

....

....

....

Exam-style questions

1 A student goes to school in an area with 'hard' water, which has a high concentration of dissolved calcium compounds.

They wanted to work out the mass of calcium compounds dissolved in 100 cm³ of tap water from the school laboratory.

a) Describe how the student could accurately measure the mass of dissolved solid in a sample of water. **[6]**

....
....
....
....
....
....
....
....
....
....
....
....
....
....
....
....
....
....
....

b) Describe two tests the student could perform to confirm that the solid residue from the water contains calcium ions.

Give the expected result of the test if calcium ions were present. **[3]**

....
....
....
....
....
....

c) The student adds barium chloride to the water sample. A white precipitate is formed. Adding hydrochloric acid and silver nitrate to the sample did not give a visible reaction.

Name the compound present in the water. **[1]**

....

Chemistry

d) The student writes that the water tested is 'potable, but not pure'.

Explain the difference between potable water and pure water. **[2]**

....

....

....

....

2 Rainwater can be collected to water plants in gardens and on farms.

Three samples of rainwater were tested with universal indicator, as shown in the table.

Sample location	Indicator colour	Approximate pH
countryside	yellow–green	
city centre	yellow	
steel works	red	

a) Complete the table by estimating the pH value of the rainwater samples. **[1]**

b) All rainwater is weakly acidic due to small amounts of dissolved carbon dioxide reacting with the rainwater as it falls through the atmosphere.

Use this information, and your knowledge, to explain the difference in pH between the countryside and city centre samples. **[2]**

....

....

....

c) The sample for the area close to the steel works is found to contain sulfuric acid (H_2SO_4). This is commonly known as 'acid rain'.

Name the gas given off at the steel works that is likely to cause the formation of sulfuric acid. **[1]**

....

d) Sulfuric acid is a strong acid. It completely ionises to form two hydrogen ions (H^+) and a negatively charged ion in solution.

Name this negatively charged ion. **[1]**

....

e) Describe a test that could be used to confirm the presence of the ion identified in part d in sulfuric acid solution; include the observation for a positive test in your answer. **[2]**

....

....

....

[Total = ... / 19 marks]

Further application

1   A group of students decided to perform chemical tests on samples of water from a local spring to see if it was safe to drink.

The spring water runs through on abandoned mine before emerging from the ground, so it likely contains some form of metal ion.

The students decided to perform the sodium hydroxide test on the water samples.

a) A sample of water from the mouth of the spring was tested. It produced a dark green precipitate.
    What does this tell you about the ion content of the water and the mine that it runs through?   **[2]**

    ....

    ....

    ....

    ....

    ....

b) A sample of water from a stream fed by the spring was also tested. It produced a brown precipitate.
    Write the ionic equation for the formation of this precipitate, including the correct state symbols.   **[3]**

    ....

c) Explain why the type of ions in the stream has changed after the water has been above ground for a period of time.
    You should assume that no other iron ions have dissolved in the water before the second test.   **[3]**

    ....

    ....

    ....

    ....

    ....

    ....

2   A water sample collected from a local stream is suspected to be contaminated with lithium carbonate.

a) Complete the table to show the expected observations for tests on lithium carbonate.   **[1]**

Sample	Add universal indicator	Flame test	Add hydrochloric acid
Lithium carbonate			

b) The concentration of lithium carbonate can be determined by titrating the water sample against hydrochloric acid. Balance the equation for the reaction of lithium carbonate with hydrochloric acid. **[1]**

..... Li_2CO_3 + ... HCl → ..... $LiCl$ + ... H_2O + ... CO_2

25 cm³ of the water sample was titrated against 0.1 mol/dm³ of hydrochloric acid solution. This table shows the results.

	Repeat 1	Repeat 2	Repeat 3	Mean
End volume / cm³	15.15	30.35	45.50	
Start volume / cm³	0.05	15.15	30.35	
Titre / cm³				

c) Complete the results table. **[2]**

(HT) **d)** Calculate the concentration of lithium carbonate in the water sample. **[3]**

(HT) **e)** A solution of another Group 1 metal carbonate, M_2CO_3, was made by dissolving 0.345 g of the unknown carbonate in 25 cm³ of water.

12.5 cm³ of 0.4 mol/dm³ hydrochloric acid was needed to fully neutralise all of the carbonate.

Calculate the relative formula mass (M_r) of the Group 1 metal carbonate and use this information to calculate the relative atomic mass of the unknown metal. **[4]**

> **Tip**
>
> To identify the unknown metal in the metal carbonate, you must subtract the relative atomic masses of any elements that you know are *definitely* there. The remaining mass must, therefore, be the unknown metal.

[Total = ... / 19 marks]

Required practical 14: Investigating specific heat capacity

In this practical you will determine the specific heat capacity of copper, or another metal, using an electrical heater. The copper block will be supplied with a calculable amount of energy, resulting in a rise in temperature. The specific heat capacity of a material is the energy required to increase the temperature of 1 kg of the material by 1°C.

It is defined by the equation:

$$E = mc\Delta\theta$$

where

- E is the energy supplied in joules, J
- m is the mass of the sample in kilograms, kg
- c is the specific heat capacity of the material, in J/kg°C
- $\Delta\theta$ is the temperature change of the sample, °C

Aim

Determine the specific heat capacity of one or more materials. The investigation will involve linking the decrease of one energy store (or work done) to the increase in temperature and subsequent increase in thermal energy stored.

Equipment

- Copper (or other metal) block with two bores
- Insulating holder for the block
- Heatproof mat
- Thermometer
- Stopwatch
- Mass balance
- 12 V power supply
- Electrical heating element
- Petroleum jelly
- Voltmeter
- Ammeter
- Connecting wires

Method

Tip

Read the method thoroughly from beginning to end before starting the experiment. If there is a step that you do not understand, ask your teacher for help before starting to avoid any additional risk.

1 Use the mass balance to find the mass of the metal block, in kilograms.

2 Place the thermometer into the smaller bore in the metal block. Measure the initial temperature.

3 Place the metal block into an insulating holder. Place it onto a heatproof mat.

4 Lubricate the electrical heating element with petroleum jelly. Insert it into the larger bore in the copper block.

5 Connect the electrical heating element to the power supply. Add an ammeter and voltmeter to the circuit, as shown in the diagram.

6 Switch the power supply on and start the stopwatch. Record the values of voltage and current for the heating circuit by taking readings from the voltmeter and ammeter, respectively. Put this data in the **observations** section.

7 Wait for the temperature of the copper block to rise by 20–30 °C.

8 Switch off the power supply and stop the stopwatch. Record the time.

9 Wait until the temperature on the thermometer stops rising. Record the final temperature of the copper block.

10 Allow the experiment to cool down before you put the equipment away or repeat the experiment.

Further information can be found in **AQA GCSE (9–1) Combined Science Student Book** on these pages:
- 268–270: Energy changes in systems
- 325–326: Specific heat capacity.

Key equations

$$\text{power (W)} = \text{current (A)} \times \frac{\text{potential difference (V)}}{}$$

$$\text{energy transferred (J)} = \text{power (W)} \times \text{time (s)}$$

$$E = mc\Delta\theta$$

Health and safety

- The electrical heating element will get very hot, as will the copper block when heated. Be very careful when handling them; wait until they have cooled before you take the equipment apart.
- Certain types of immersion heater may explode if the seal is broken and water gets inside.

Maths opportunities

- Using an appropriate number of significant figures
- Changing the subject of an equation
- Substituting numerical values into algebraic equations using appropriate units for physical quantities
- Plotting two variables from experimental or other data

Tip

Adding a small amount of petroleum jelly to the thermometer creates a better contact with the copper block for thermal conduction.

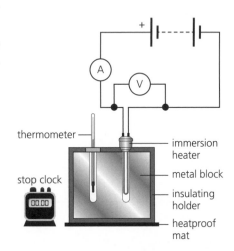

Observations

1 Complete this table with your results.

Mass of block / kg	
Initial temperature of block / °C	
Final temperature of block / °C	
Change in temperature of block / °C	
Time the electrical heater was switched on for / s	
Current running through the heating circuit / A	
Voltage across the electrical heater / V	

2 Calculate the power of your electrical heater, in W, using the equation $P = I \times V$.

3 Calculate the energy supplied to the copper block, in J, using the equation $E = P \times t$.

4 Calculate the specific heat capacity of the copper block, in J/kg °C, using the equation $E = mc\Delta\theta$.

Evaluation

5 The specific heat capacity of copper is about 385 J/kg °C.

How close is your value to this figure? What could account for the difference?

....

....

....

Exam-style questions

1 a) State what is meant by the term *internal energy*. **[1]**

....

....

b) Describe how the motion of the molecules in a solid changes when it is heated. **[2]**

....

....

2 A water balloon containing 0.40 kg of water at 20 °C is placed in a freezer. The temperature of the water drops to 0 °C in 20 mins.

The specific heat capacity of water is 4200 J/kg °C

a) Calculate the energy lost by the water as it cools to 0 °C. **[2]**

....

....

....

....

b) Calculate the average rate at which the water is losing energy, in J/s. **[1]**

....

....

....

....

3 An electrical heater is used to heat a well-insulated, 3.0 kg block of unknown metal.

The temperature of the block was taken at regular intervals, as shown in this table.

Time / s	0	60	120	180	240	300
Temperature / °C	20.6	23.5	27.4	30.5	33.6	37.4
Work done / kJ	0					15

a) The power of the electrical heater is 50 W. Complete the table. **[4]**

b) Plot a graph of *temperature* (*y*-axis) against *work done* (*x*-axis). [4]

c) Using the gradient of your graph, or otherwise, determine a value for the specific heat capacity of the unknown metal. [3]

For your graph, $\dfrac{1}{\text{gradient}} = \text{mass} \times \text{specific heat capacity}$

....

....

....

4 The specific heat capacities of water and copper are:

specific heat capacity of water = 4200 J/kg °C

specific heat capacity of copper = 385 J/kg °C

a) Calculate the energy needed to heat a copper pan of mass 0.40 kg from 20 °C to 100 °C. [2]

....

....

....

....

b) Calculate the energy needed to heat 1.25 kg of water from 20 °C to 100 °C. [2]

....

....

....

....

[Total = ... / 21 marks]

Further application

1 In order to measure the temperature of a blowtorch, a piece of iron of mass 0.22 kg is heated in the blowtorch flame for several minutes. The piece of iron is then dropped into an insulated beaker filled with 0.50 kg of water. The temperature rise of the water is measured. The specific heat capacities of iron and water are:

specific heat capacity of iron = 490 J/kg °C

specific heat capacity of water = 4200 J/kg °C

   a) Give **two** ways to improve the resolution of your measurements.   **[2]**

     1. ....

       ....

     2. ....

       ....

   b) State **one** risk associated with this experiment and a method to reduce this risk.   **[2]**

       ....

       ....

   c) Why does the beaker of water have to be insulated?   **[1]**

       ....

       ....

       ....

       ....

   d) Calculate the thermal energy gained by the water if the temperature of the water rose from 15 °C to 40 °C.   **[2]**

   e) State the thermal energy lost by the iron.   **[1]**

       ....

   f) Calculate the decrease in temperature of the piece of iron as it is plunged into the water.   **[2]**

   g) Using your answer to the previous question, find the temperature reached by the iron in the flame and hence the temperature of the blowtorch.   **[1]**

       ....

       ....

2 Water, of mass 300 g and temperature 4.0 °C, is poured into a glass. The glass has a mass of 350 g and initial temperature of 25.0 °C.

specific heat capacity of water = 4200 J/kg °C

specific heat capacity of glass = 840 J/ kg °C

a) Show that the final temperature of the water and glass, when they reach **thermal equilibrium**, is approximately 8 °C. [6]

Key term 🔑	Tip 💡
Thermal equilibrium: two substances in thermal equilibrium are at the same temperature.	The thermal energy transferred away from the glass is gained by the water. Both objects will also have the same final temperature.

b) Ice is added to cool the water and the glass to 2.0 °C.

Calculate the amount of energy that the ice will gain. Give your answer to two significant figures.

> **Tip** 💡
> Remember that the ice will gain energy from the water and the glass.

[3]

c) The ice had a starting temperature of −3.0 °C.

Calculate the minimum mass of ice needed to cool the water and glass to 2.0 °C. [6]

specific heat capacity of ice = 2108 J/kg °C

latent heat of fusion of ice = 334 000 J/kg

> **Key equation** x+y=z
> energy required = mass × specific latent heat

> **Tip** 💡
> Think about what has to happen to the ice to get it to 2 °C.

[Total = ... / 26 marks]

Required practical 15: Investigating the factors affecting the resistance of electrical circuits

Resistance is simply a measure of how difficult it is for an electric current to flow through a component or circuit. The more difficult it is for the electrons to pass through the circuit, the higher the resistance will be. It is important to understand the resistance of a circuit and its components as it ensures each part is getting the correct amount of potential difference and **current** for their purpose. Get it wrong, and components might not work or could break.

Resistance can be calculated using **Ohm's law**:

$$R = \frac{V}{I}$$

where

- R is resistance, measured in ohms, Ω
- V is voltage (**potential difference**), measured in volts, V
- I is current, measured in amps, A

Further information can be found in **AQA GCSE (9–1) Combined Science Student Book** on these pages:
- 294–296: Current and charge
- 296: Ammeters and voltmeters
- 296–297: Resistance.

Key terms

Current: a flow of electrical charge; the size of the electric current is the rate of flow of electrical charge; it is measured in amperes (A).

Ohm's law: the current flowing through a resistor at a constant temperature is directly proportional to the voltage across the resistor.

Potential difference (p.d.): a measure of the work done, or energy transferred to a component, by each coulomb of charge that passes through it; it is measured in volts (V).

Series: in a series circuit, components are connected one after another in a complete circuit loop.

Parallel: in a parallel circuit, two or more components are connected to the same points in the circuit.

Health and safety

- Ensure that wires are properly insulated and do not use multiple batteries if you are using low-voltage lamps, as this could cause them to blow.
- Wires may get hot with larger currents.

Maths opportunities

- Recognising and using expressions in standard form
- Using an appropriate number of significant figures
- Finding arithmetic means
- Plotting two variables from experimental or other data
- Changing the subject of an equation
- Substituting numerical values into algebraic equations using appropriate units for physical quantities

Key equations

Ohm's law: $R = \dfrac{V}{I}$

Aim

*Investigate the factors affecting the resistance of electrical circuits including the length of a wire at constant temperature (Part A) and combinations of resistors in **series** and **parallel** (Part B).*

Equipment

- Length of wire mounted on a metre rule (e.g. 0.5 mm in diameter)
- Wires
- Crocodile clips
- Battery
- Two resistors
- Voltmeter
- Ammeter

Method

In **Part A**, you will be investigating how the length of a wire affects its resistance.

In **Part B**, you will be investigating how the arrangement of components (such as resistors) in *series* and *parallel* affects the resistance of the circuit.

Part A: Length of a wire

1 Set your equipment up as shown in this diagram.

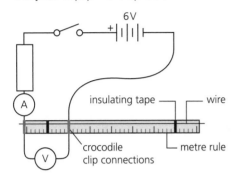

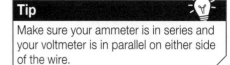

Tip

Make sure your ammeter is in series and your voltmeter is in parallel on either side of the wire.

2 Attach one crocodile clip to the end of the wire that is mounted on the metre rule. Attach the other crocodile clip 0.1 m along the wire.

3 There should now be a reading on both your ammeter and voltmeter. Add both these values to your results table in the **observations** section.

4 Move the second crocodile clip along the wire and take measurements every 0.1 m, up to 1 m. You should complete the results table.

Tip

If no values show on your ammeter and/or voltmeter, check that you have set it up correctly and that none of the components are broken.

Part B: Resistors in series and parallel

1 Set up your circuit for a single resistor, as shown in the first circuit diagram. If the circuit is set up correctly, there will be readings on both the voltmeter and ammeter.

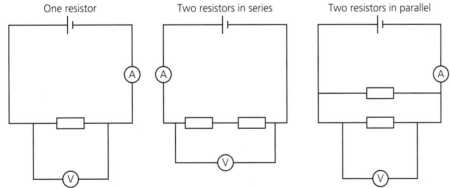

2 Record these reading in the results table in the **observations** section.

3 Calculate the resistance of the circuit using Ohm's law.

4 Add in a second resistor, in series, as shown in the second circuit diagram. Take readings and add them to the results table.

5 Move the second resistor so that it is now in parallel, as shown in the third circuit diagram. Take a final set of readings and add to the results table.

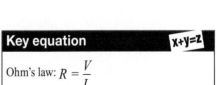

Key equation

Ohm's law: $R = \dfrac{V}{I}$

Observations

Part A

Length / m	0.1	0.2	0.3	0.4	0.5	0.6	0.7	0.8	0.9	1.0
Current / A										
Potential difference / V										
Resistance / Ω										

Part B

Arrangement	Potential difference / V	Current / A	Resistance / Ω
One resistor			
Two resistors in series			
Two resistors in parallel			

Conclusions

Part A

1   Plot a graph of *length* (*x*-axis) against *resistance* (*y*-axis). Draw a line of best fit.

2   Look at your graph. What pattern do you notice? Suggest a reason why your graph has this pattern.

....

....

3 Suggest why your line of best fit does not pass through the origin.

....

....

....

Part B

4 How, and why, does the current change as you add resistors in series?

....

....

....

....

5 What happens to the current as you add resistors in parallel? Give a reason for your answer.

....

....

....

....

6 Suggest what would happen if you added a third resistor in series.

....

....

7 Suggest what would happen if you added a third resistor in parallel.

....

....

Evaluation

Part A

8 Describe **two** ways you could improve the accuracy of your experiment.

....

....

....

....

Part B

9 Why does the voltage of the circuit stay the same for each arrangement? How would you increase or decrease it?

....

....

....

....

Exam-style questions

1   A student set up a circuit as shown in this diagram. They used three lamps of identical resistance.

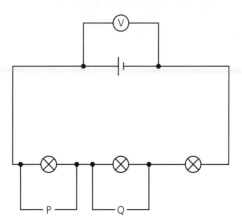

a)   The voltmeter across the power supply measures 6.0 V. Calculate the potential difference reading at **P**.   [1]

....

....

....

b)   The current in the circuit is 0.5 A. Calculate the resistance of one of the lamps.   [3]

....

....

....

....

c)   Calculate the power of one of the lamps.   [2]

....

....

....

d)   Calculate the total energy transferred to all three lamps over the course of 3 minutes.   [3]

....

....

....

....

e)   The voltmeter reading at **Q** actually reads 2.20 V. Identify the measurement error.   [1]

....

....

f)   Give a possible reason for this error.   [1]

....

....

[Total = ... / 11 marks]

Physics

Further application

1 This equation shows the relationship between resistance of a metal wire and three factors: resistivity, length and cross sectional area.

$$\text{resistance} = \frac{\text{resistivity} \times \text{length}}{\text{cross sectional area}}$$

where

resistance is measured in ohms, Ω

resistivity is measured in ohm metres, Ωm

length is measured in metres, m

cross sectional area is measured in square metres, m²

Rearrange the equation to make *resistivity* the subject.   [1]

> **Key term**
>
> **Cross sectional area:** the two-dimensional area you would see when you cut into a wire.

2 A student wishes to measure the resistivity of a cylindrical copper wire.

They have an ammeter, a battery, a switch, a variable resistor and a voltmeter.

a) Complete a circuit diagram, using the equipment listed, which will enable the student to determine the resistivity of the copper wire. The diagram has been started for you.   [2]

$$\dashv\!|\!-\!-\!|\!\vdash$$

b) The student plans to use a metre ruler to measure the length of the copper wire.

Suggest why this would **not** be suitable for measuring the cross sectional area of the wire. Suggest an alternative measuring device.   [2]

....

....

....

c) The radius of the wire is measured as 7.4×10^{-5} m. Calculate the cross-sectional area. **[2]**

> **Key equation** x+y=z
>
> area of a circle $= \pi \times r^2$
>
> where
>
> r is the radius measured in metres, m

d) When a potential difference of 2.0 V is put across a 50 cm length of the copper wire, a current of 4.0 A is measured. Calculate the resistivity of copper. **[5]**

[Total = ... / 12 marks]

Required practical 16: Investigating the *I–V* characteristics of a variety of circuit elements

I–V characteristics are current–voltage graphs that show how the **current** across a component varies as the voltage across it is increased or decreased. Different components have differently shaped *I–V* characteristics which you can see when plotted on a graph. These graphs can also be used to calculate the resistance of a component at different voltages, by using the gradient of the characteristic.

Aim

Use circuit diagrams to construct appropriate circuits to investigate the I–V characteristics of a variety of circuit elements including a filament lamp, a diode and a fixed resistor at constant temperature.

Equipment

- Variable power supply
- Voltmeter
- Ammeter, milliammeter or multimeter
- Fixed resistor
- Filament lamp
- Diode
- Wires

Method

1 Ensure that the power supply is switched off. Set up your circuit, as shown in the diagram, with the fixed resistor where it says 'component'.

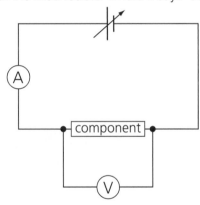

2 Set the voltage to between 1–2 V. Turn the power supply on and record the current through the circuit (using the ammeter) and the voltage across the component (using the voltmeter, **not** the dial on the power supply). Use the 'positive' section of the table in the **observations** section.

3 Increase the voltage on the power supply by 1–2 V. Record the ammeter and voltmeter readings again. Repeat until you have six readings, up to about 12 V.

4 Turn the power supply off and switch around the two wires connecting it to the circuit. This will cause the current to flow around the circuit in the opposite (negative) direction.

5 Repeat steps 2–3, using your readings to complete the 'negative' section of the results table.

6 Repeat steps 1–5, replacing the fixed resistor with the filament lamp.

7 Repeat steps 1–5, replacing the fixed resistor with the diode.

Key terms

Potential difference (p.d.): a measure of the work done, or energy transferred to a component, by each **coulomb** of charge that passes through it; it is measured in volts (V).

Coulomb: the measurement unit for charge; each electron has a tiny charge of -1.6×10^{-19} C.

Resolution: the smallest possible quantity being measured by a measuring instrument that will show a noticeable change in the reading.

Further information can be found in **AQA GCSE (9–1) Combined Science Student Book** on these pages:

- 298–300: Current–potential difference characteristic graphs.

Key term

Current: a flow of electrical charge; the size of the electric current is the rate of flow of electrical charge; it is measured in amperes (A).

Health and safety

- Care should be taken as you increase the voltage of the power supply, as components (particularly the filament lamp) are likely to get quite hot. Check wires and leads for damage before use.
- Suitable components are a 47 Ω resistor and a maximum 12 V diode or LED.

Maths opportunities $\sqrt{2^3+1}$

- Using an appropriate number of significant figures
- Using a scatter diagram to identify a correlation between two variables
- Understanding that $y = mx + c$ represents a linear relationship
- Plotting two variables from experimental or other data
- Finding the arithmetic mean of a set of data

Key equations $x+y=z$

$$\text{resistance } (\Omega) = \frac{\text{potential difference } (V)}{\text{current } (A)}$$

$$\text{gradient} = \frac{\text{change in } y}{\text{change in } x}$$

For an *I–V* characteristic with a constant gradient, change in *y* is change in *I* (current) and change in *x* is change in *V* (voltage), so

$$\text{gradient} = \frac{I}{V}$$

$$\text{gradient} = \frac{1}{\text{resistance}}$$

Tip

When measuring the characteristics of the diode, you will need to put a fixed resistor in series with the diode. Otherwise, there would be too high a current running through it. Due to the low currents through the diode, a milliammeter will need to be used. This is because a milliammeter has a higher **resolution** than an ammeter.

Observations

	Fixed resistor		Filament lamp		Diode	
	Potential difference / V	Current / A	Potential difference / V	Current / A	Potential difference / V	Current / A
Positive						
Negative						

1   For each component, plot a graph of *Potential difference* (*x*-axis) against *Current* (*y*-axis). Draw lines or curves of best fit.

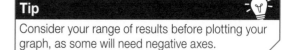

Tip

Consider your range of results before plotting your graph, as some will need negative axes.

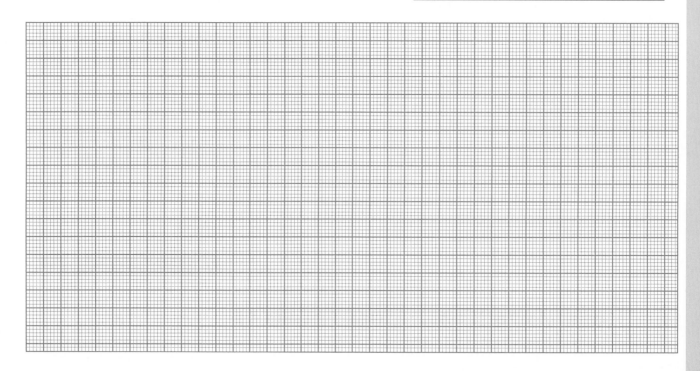

Physics

2 Calculate the resistance of your fixed resistor.

3 Label, on your graph, the parts of the filament lamp $I–V$ characteristic which show the points at which the lamp has the highest and lowest resistance. Explain why this is the case.

....

....

....

Conclusions

4 Why does the $I–V$ characteristic of the fixed resistor prove Ohm's law?

....

....

5 Describe what an $I–V$ characteristic of a fixed resistor with a higher resistance would look like.

....

....

Evaluation

6 Your teacher will explain to you (or show you) what the shapes of your graphs should be.

Compare your graphs to what was expected. Evaluate the reasons for any differences.

....

....

....

....

....

....

Exam-style questions

1 A student was given this *I–V* characteristic graph.

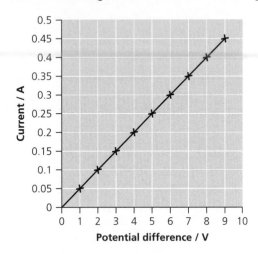

a) Which component does the graph represent? Circle your answer. [1]

Diode   Fixed resistor   Filament lamp   LED

b) Determine the potential difference required to produce a current of 0.3 A. [1]

....

....

c) Assuming the gradient remains constant, predict the current through the component for a potential
difference of 14 V. [1]

....

....

d) Calculate the resistance of this component. [3]

....

....

....

2 A student was investigating how the current through a filament lamp varies with potential difference across it.
This table shows the student's results.

Potential difference / V	Current / A			Mean current
	Repeat 1	Repeat 2	Repeat 3	
0.50	0.24	0.28	0.12	
1.50	0.61	0.63	0.62	
3.00	0.96	1.01	1.00	
4.50	1.28	1.28	1.31	
6.00	1.47	1.48	1.52	
7.50	1.52	1.70	1.75	
12.00	2.00	2.02	2.04	

a) Identify and circle **two** anomalous results. Give a reason for why these anomalies may have occurred. **[3]**

....

....

b) Use the remaining results to calculate the mean values of current. Complete the table. **[2]**

c) Determine which potential difference gave the current values with the smallest range. **[1]**

....

d) Plot a graph of *Potential difference* (*x*-axis) against *Current* (*y*-axis). Draw a curve of best fit. **[4]**

e) Explain why the characteristic has the shape shown in your graph, as the potential difference is increased from zero. **[5]**

....

....

....

....

....

....

....

....

[Total = ... / 21 marks]

Further application

1 A thermistor is a component that changes its resistance with temperature.

A student is planning to investigate what this relationship is.

They plan to set up a circuit using a battery, voltmeter, ammeter and thermistor.

a) Draw the circuit diagram that the student will need to construct for this experiment. [3]

b) Design a method to measure the resistance of the thermistor for a range of temperatures from 0 °C to 100 °C.

Mention any additional equipment required. [5]

Physics

c) Complete the resistance column in this table below. Describe any pattern that emerges. **[4]**

> **Tip**
>
> Be careful of unit suffixes appearing in questions as they are easy to miss.

Temperature / °C	Potential difference / V	Current / mA	Resistance / Ω
5	12.0	0.54	
15	11.9	0.82	
25	12.0	1.20	
35	12.0	1.73	
45	11.9	2.42	
65	12.0	4.63	
85	12.0	8.25	

d) The student then decides they want to set up a temperature sensor circuit using the thermistor as a **potential divider**.

They want an alarm to sound when the temperature gets too high (and, therefore, it receives a high potential difference).

At which position, X or Y, should they place the alarm? Explain why the alarm needs to be placed at this position. **[4]**

> **Key term**
>
> **Potential dividers:** 'split up' the voltage within a circuit, so that parts of a circuit only get the voltage they need; they are usually made up of two or more resistors arranged in series across a power supply.

....

....

....

....

....

[Total = ... / 16 marks]

Required practical 17: Determining the density of solids and liquids

Density is a measure of the mass of a given volume of a material, usually 1 cm³ or 1 m³. Density is an important way to compare the masses of materials of different volumes. For example, a steel spoon has greater density than a wooden table, but the table is heavier. In general, solids and liquids have greater densities than gases. Knowing an object's density is a good way of determining what it is made from.

Aim

*Use appropriate apparatus to make and record the measurements needed to determine the densities of regular and irregular solid objects and liquids. Volume should be determined from the dimensions of regularly shaped objects, and by a **displacement technique** for irregularly shaped objects.*

Key equation

$$\text{density} = \frac{\text{mass}}{\text{volume}} \text{ or } \rho = \frac{m}{V}$$

where
- ρ is the density of the object, measured in kg/m³
- m is the mass of the object, measured in kg
- V is the volume of the object, measured in m³

Equipment

- Cubes or cuboids of suitable material (such as wood)
- Irregularly shaped solids
- Measuring cylinder
- Water

- Liquid to test (such as water)
- Mass balance
- Ruler
- Micrometer or Vernier calliper

Method

Part A: Finding the density of a regular solid

1 Place the object on the mass balance. Record its mass in the results table in the **observations** section. Make sure you convert the mass into kilograms if necessary.
2 Measure the length of the three sides of the object. Record these in the results table. Remember to convert lengths from cm to m.
3 Calculate the volume. Record it in the results table.
4 Calculate the density of the object by dividing the mass by the volume.

Part B: Finding the density of an irregular solid

For this object, you will find the volume by the displacement method.

1 Place the object on the mass balance. Record its mass in the results table in the **observations** section. Make sure you convert the mass into kilograms if necessary.
2 Roughly half fill the measuring cylinder with water. Record the volume of the liquid in the results table.
3 Place the irregular object into the measuring cylinder. The water level should rise. Record the water level in the results table.
4 Find the difference between the two water levels – this is equal to the volume of the object.
5 Calculate the density of the object by dividing the mass by the volume.

Further information can be found in **AQA GCSE (9–1) Combined Science Student Book** on these pages:
- 319–322: Density
- 323: Density of solids, liquids and gases.

Health and safety

There are no major safety concerns with this experiment, but be careful to wipe up any spilt water to avoid slippages.

Maths opportunities

- Using an appropriate number of significant figures
- Measuring lengths and volumes
- Multiplication and division
- Calculating the volumes of cubes

Key term

Displacement technique: used to find the volume of an object by measuring the volume of water displaced (pushed up or removed) by the object.

Key equation

$$\text{volume} = \text{length} \times \text{width} \times \text{height}$$

Tip

When dealing with water, make sure to measure the mass of the object when it is dry. You may need paper towels or similar to dry the objects.

Part C: Finding the density of a liquid

1 Place an empty measuring cylinder on the mass balance. Record its mass in the results table in the **observations** section. Make sure you convert the mass into kilograms if necessary.
2 Fill the cylinder with the liquid. Read the volume, convert it into m³ and record it in the results table.
3 Find the mass of the measuring cylinder, including the liquid, using the mass balance. Record its mass in the results table. Make sure you convert the mass into kilograms if necessary.
4 Find the mass of the liquid by taking the mass of the empty measuring cylinder away from the mass of the measuring cylinder with the liquid.
5 Calculate the density of the liquid by dividing the mass of the liquid by its volume.

Observations

Part A

Object	Mass / kg	Length / m	Width / m	Depth / m	Volume / m³	Density / kg/m³

Tip
1 kg = 1000 g so, to convert grams to kilograms, divide by 1000.

Tip
1 m = 100 cm so, to convert centimetres to metres, divide by 100.

Tip
The measuring cylinder may have ml on its scale.
1 ml = 1 cm³
1 000 000 cm³ = 1 m³
To convert cm³ to m³, divide by 1 000 000.

Part B

Object	Mass / kg	Initial volume of water / cm³	Final volume of water / cm³	Volume of displaced water / cm³	Volume of object / m³	Density / kg/m³

Part C

Object	Mass of cylinder / kg	Mass of cylinder + liquid / kg	Mass of liquid / kg	Volume of liquid / m³	Density / kg/m³

Conclusion

1 Imagine that you completed the above experiment using two blocks of steel. One of the blocks was twice the volume of the other. How would the two results differ and why?

....

....

....

....

Evaluation

2 Water has a density of 1000 kg/m³. How does your value compare with this? Suggest why any differences might have occurred.

....

....

....

3 Suggest how you could increase the precision of your measurements of a liquid.

....

....

4 Suggest how you could ensure the accuracy of your value for density of a regular solid.

....

....

Exam-style questions

1 A student finds a cube of metal and wants to find out what it is made from. They take a measurement of each side and measure the mass.

Using their measurements and the table below, determine which type of metal they have found. **[4]**

length of cube = 1.5 cm

mass of cube = 24 g

Substance	Antimony	Zinc	Iron	Copper	Gold
Density / kg/m³	6700	7100	7900	8900	19300

....

....

....

....

....

....

Type of metal: ....

2 A student noticed that an egg sinks in pure water. So, they conducted an experiment to determine the density of the egg.

The student measured 1000 cm³ of pure water into a large beaker. They added 10 g of salt into the water and stirred it until it dissolved. Dissolving the salt in the water increased the mass of the saltwater without affecting its volume. They then added the egg.

The table shows their results.

Mass of dissolved salt / g	0.0	10.0	20.0	30.0	40.0	50.0	60.0
Sink or float?	Sink	Sink	Sink	Sink	Float	Float	Float

a) Describe what happened to the density of the saltwater as more salt was added. **[1]**

....

....

b) State the independent variable of the experiment. **[1]**

....

....

c) Calculate the mass of the water used in the experiment. **[3]**

Density of pure water = 1 g/cm³

....

....

....

....

d) The student decides that the mass of dissolved salt needed to just about make the egg float must be 35 g.

Give a value for the uncertainty of this measurement.

35 ± .... g   [1]

e) The true value of mass of salt needed for the density of the saltwater and egg to be equal is 31 g.

Calculate the true density of the egg.   [3]

$$\text{density of saltwater} = \frac{\text{mass of water} + \text{mass of salt}}{\text{volume of saltwater}}$$

While salt can still be dissolved, volume of water = volume of salt water.

....

....

....

....

....

[Total = ... / 13 marks]

Further application

1 Bronze is an alloy of copper and tin. It is made from 88% copper by volume and 12% tin by volume.

density of copper = 8.9×10^3 kg/m³

density of tin = 7.3×10^3 kg/m³

a) Determine the mass of copper and the mass of tin required to make a block of bronze of volume 1.6×10^{-3} m³. **[5]**

b) Calculate the density of bronze. **[2]**

2 Archimedes was asked by his king to determine whether a crown was made from pure gold. He suspected that the goldsmith had short-changed him by mixing in other metals.

Describe a method, without damaging the crown, that Archimedes could use to find out whether the king had been cheated. **[3]**

[Total = ... / 10 marks]

Required practical 18: Investigating the relationship between force and extension

When a force is applied to a spring, it will extend or compress (depending on the direction of the force). How much the spring will extend or compress depends on both the size of the force applied and the spring (or force) constant of the spring, k. The stiffer the spring, the harder it is to extend or compress it, and the higher the value of k. This relationship can be shown mathematically using Hooke's law:

$$F = ke$$

where

- F is the force applied to the spring, measured in newtons, N
- k is the spring constant, measured in newtons per metre, N/m
- e is the **extension** of the spring, measured in metres, m

> **Key term**
>
> **Extension:** the difference between the stretched and unstretched lengths of a spring.

To calculate the force of weight applied to a spring, the following equation can be used:

$$W = mg$$

where

- W is the weight, measured in newtons, N
- m is the mass, measured in kilograms, kg
- g is the gravitational field strength, measured in newtons per kilogram, N/kg (on Earth, this is 9.81 N/kg)

Aim

Investigate the relationship between force and extension for a spring.

Equipment

- Spring
- 100 g mass hanger
- Five 100 g masses
- Metre rule
- 30 cm ruler
- Clamp stand
- Two clamps
- Two bosses
- Eye protection

Method

1. Put on your eye protection.
2. Set up the equipment as shown in the diagram. First, you should hang the spring on the clamp without the mass hanger being attached.
3. Measure the original length of the spring in metres. It is useful to use the 30 cm ruler as a pointer here to reduce **parallax error**. Record this in the results table in the **observations** section.
4. Complete the first column of the results table. As there is no mass being hung from the spring, there is no force and, therefore, no extension.
5. Making sure that your feet are not underneath the spring, hang the 100 g mass hanger onto the spring. You have now applied a force of 1 N to it. Let the spring settle.
6. Use the 30 cm ruler to measure the new length of the spring. Find the extension by subtracting the original length of the spring from this value. Record this in the results table.
7. Add a 100 g mass onto the hanger and repeat steps 5–6.
8. Repeat until you have added at least five 100 g masses onto the mass hanger. Take care not to add too many masses onto the spring, as the spring could overextend and deform permanently.

Further information can be found in **AQA GCSE (9–1) Combined Science Student Book** on these pages:

- 571–574: Forces and elasticity (or *CS 2: 215–218*).

Health and safety

- You should wear eye protection, in case the masses fall off the spring and the spring snaps into your eye.
- You should also ensure that your feet are never under the masses, in case the masses fall onto them.

Maths opportunities

- Using an appropriate number of significant figures
- Finding arithmetic means
- Understanding that $y = mx + c$ represents a linear relationship
- Plotting two variables from experimental or other data

Key equations

$$F = ke$$
$$W = mg$$

$$\text{extension} = \text{extended} - \text{original}$$
$$e \qquad\quad \text{length} \qquad \text{length}$$

Tip

In this practical, you will use 100 g masses (approximate weight = 1 N).

$$W = mg$$
$$W = 0.1\,\text{kg} \times 9.8\,\text{N/kg} = 0.98\,\text{N} \approx 1\,\text{N}$$

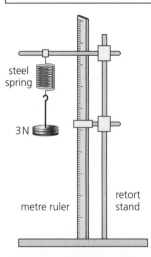

steel spring

3 N

metre ruler

retort stand

Key term

Parallax error: when looking at an object you are using to measure a value, it can appear in a different position than its actual position because of your line of sight.

Observations

Natural length of spring = ... m

Mass / kg						
Force / N						
Extension / m						

1 Plot a graph of *force* (*y*-axis) against *extension* (*x*-axis) for your spring. Draw a line of best fit – it should be a straight line through the origin.

2 Calculate the gradient of the line of best fit – this is the value of the spring constant, *k*, for your spring.

> **Tip**
>
> To calculate the gradient of a straight line, find two points on the line of best fit. Calculate the change in the *y* coordinate (force) and the change in the *x* coordinate (extension).
>
> $$\text{gradient} = \frac{\text{change in } y}{\text{change in } x}$$

Conclusions

3 Hooke's law states that the extension of a spring is directly proportional to the force applied to it. Explain how your graph proves this statement.

....

....

4 Describe the force–extension graph of a spring with a higher spring constant.

....

....

5 Describe how the graph would look different if you used spring length rather than extension.

....

....

....

6 Suggest what would happen to the extension of your spring if you doubled the amount of force you were applying.

....

....

....

7 If you add too many masses to the spring, it will overextend and permanently deform. Suggest what a force–extension graph would look like for this extension.

....

....

....

Evaluation

8 Usually, the independent variable is plotted on the *x*-axis of a graph and the dependent variable is plotted on the *y*-axis. In this experiment, we do the opposite. Suggest why.

....

....

....

9 You may have found that your line of best fit does not go through all your plotted points. Describe how you could improve the accuracy of your measurements.

....

....

....

Physics

Exam-style questions

1 An astronaut is conducting an experiment into the extension of an elastic band on the Moon. They do this by hanging masses onto the end of the band and measuring the extension with a ruler.

The gravitational field strength on the Moon, g, is 1.6 N/kg.

a) Using the data in the table, and the key equations, calculate the missing values.   **[2]**

Mass / g	625	938		1560	1870
Force / N	1.00		2.00	2.50	3.00
Extension / m	0.02	0.03	0.04	0.05	0.07

b) Use the results from the table to plot a graph of *force* (*y*-axis) against *extension* (*x*-axis).   **[4]**

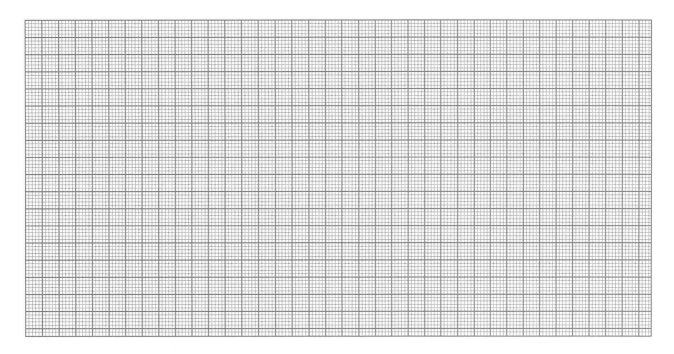

c) Use the gradient of your graph to find the spring constant, k, of the elastic band.   **[1]**

$$\text{gradient} = \frac{\text{change in } y}{\text{change in } x} = \frac{\text{change in force}}{\text{change in extension}} = k$$

....

....

....

d) Calculate the energy stored in the elastic band when extended by 30 cm. **[2]**

elastic potential energy $= \frac{1}{2} \times$ spring constant $\times$ (extension)^2

....

....

....

....

e) State the amount of work done in stretching the elastic band by 30 cm. **[1]**

....

....

....

2 This is a graph of a student's results when adding masses to a spring. Explain the shape of the graph. **[4]**

....

....

....

....

....

[Total = ... / 14 marks]

Further application

1   A student is investigating what happens to the spring constant if springs are added in **series** or in **parallel**. The student had three identical springs to test and a selection of known masses. They used this equipment to apply various forces on the springs as well as using several combinations.

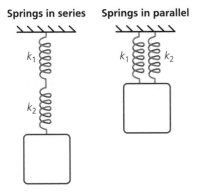

Springs in series   **Springs in parallel**

k_1 k_1 k_2

k_2

> **Key terms**
>
> **Springs in series:** when springs are added end to end.
>
> **Springs in parallel:** when springs are added side by side.

Their results are laid out in the table below.

Force / N	Extension / cm				
	One spring	Two springs in series	Three springs in series	Two springs in parallel	Three springs in parallel
0	0.0	0.0	0.0	0.0	0.0
1	2.0	4.0	6.0	1.0	0.7
2	4.0	8.0	12.0	2.0	1.3
3	6.0	12.0	18.0	3.0	2.0
4	8.0	16.0	24.0	4.0	2.7
5	10.0	20.0	30.0	5.0	3.3

a)   For each combination, calculate the spring constant, and complete the table below.   [5]

	One spring	Two springs in series	Three springs in series	Two springs in parallel	Three springs in parallel
Spring constant / N/m					

b)   Describe any patterns that you see

i)   for springs in series   [2]

....

....

....

ii) for springs in parallel. [2]

....

....

....

c) Decide which set up of springs will store the most elastic potential energy when extended by 20 cm.

Support your answer with calculations. [3]

> **Key equation** x+y=z
>
> elastic potential energy = 0.5 × spring constant × (extension)²

....

....

....

....

....

....

[Total = ... / 12 marks]

Required practical 19: Investigating factors that affect acceleration

Acceleration is the rate of change of **velocity**; it tells us how quickly or slowly an object speeds up or slows down. According to Newton's second law, the acceleration of an object depends on the force applied to it and the mass of the object itself. We can write this mathematically as:

$F = ma$

where

- F is the force applied in newtons, N
- m is the mass of the object in kilograms, kg
- a is the acceleration of the object in metres per second squared, m/s^2

This relationship tells us that acceleration is proportional to force and indirectly proportional to mass; the acceleration of an object will increase as you increase the force applied, but will decrease as you increase the mass of the object.

Aim

Investigate the effect of varying the force on the acceleration of an object of constant mass and to investigate the effect of varying the mass of an object on the acceleration produced by a constant force.

Equipment

- Dynamics trolley
- Pulley
- String
- Slotted 100 g masses and hanger
- Ticker tape
- Ticker timer
- Power supply
- Piece of carpet

- Ruler
- Two light gates
- **Data logger**
- Clamp stand and boss
- Segment of black card
- Mass balance
- Tape

Method

Part A: Varying force

1 Clamp the pulley onto the edge of a bench. Place a piece of carpet on the floor underneath. You will need to keep this in place for **Part B**.

2 Set up the ticker timer by attaching it to an a.c. power supply (6–12 V) and placing it approximately 1 m away from the pulley.

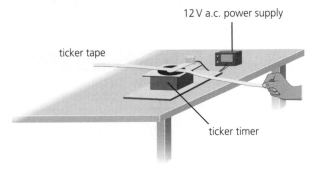

ticker tape · 12 V a.c. power supply · ticker timer

Further information can be found in **AQA GCSE (9–1) Combined Science Student Book** on these pages:

- 592–595: the relationship between resultant force and acceleration (*or CS 2: 236–239*).

Key terms

Acceleration: the rate of change of velocity.

Velocity: an object's speed in a given direction.

Health and safety

Take care when dropping the masses over the pulley – make sure that there is a piece of carpet or something similar to break their fall. Make sure your feet are not underneath.

Maths opportunities

- Using an appropriate number of significant figures
- Finding arithmetic means
- Using a scatter diagram to identify a correlation between two variables
- Plotting two variables from experimental or other data

Key equations

$$\text{speed} = \frac{\text{distance travelled}}{\text{time taken}}$$

$$\text{acceleration} = \frac{\text{change in velocity}}{\text{time taken}}$$

$$F = ma$$

Key term

Data logger: an electronic device that uses sensors to record data over time; data loggers can often take readings more frequently and to a higher resolution than other measuring devices, so they are more accurate and, therefore, better for practical work.

3   Attach a piece of string to one end of the dynamics trolley and tie a 100 g mass hanger onto the end. Tape a piece of ticker tape, approximately 1 m long, to the other end of the trolley.

4   Feed the ticker tape through the ticker timer so that the dynamics trolley is positioned next to it. See the diagram for assistance.

5   Turn the ticker timer on, then hang the mass hanger over the pulley. Let it go so that the trolley is pulled along the table.

6   Take the ticker tape off the dynamics trolley and label it 100 g or 1 N.

7   Reset the experiment by taping a new piece of ticker tape to the trolley and feeding it through the ticker timer. Add a second 100 g mass to the hanger and repeat the experiment, making sure you start the trolley from the same point each time.

8   Repeat steps 3–7 for four more masses.

9   Use your ticker tapes to complete the results table in the **observations** section.

> **Note**
> On Earth, a mass of 100 g has an approximate weight of 1 N.

Part B: Varying mass

1   Use the mass balance to find the mass of the trolley. Record this in the results table in the **observations** section.

2   Measure the length of the square of black card in metres. Record this in the results table. Stick the card onto the dynamics trolley, as shown in the diagram.

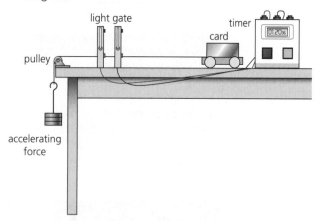

3   Set up the rest of the equipment as shown.
   • Your clamp and pulley should still be in place from **Part A**.
   • Set up the light gates and data logger according to their specific instructions. Make sure that the gates are level and will be blocked by the black card as the trolley moves past them.
   • Attach a piece of string to one end of the dynamics trolley. Tie the 100 g mass hanger onto the end.

4   Make sure that the light gates are recording data. Hang the mass hanger over the pulley. Let the hanger go so that the trolley is pulled along the table.

5   Record the information from the light gates in the results table.

6   Reset the experiment. Add a 100 g mass to the dynamics trolley itself to increase its mass and repeat the experiment for this higher mass, making sure that you start the trolley from the same point as before. Fill in the second row of your table.

7   Repeat steps 4–6 four more times, adding an extra 100 g mass onto the trolley each time.

8   Complete the results table.

> **Note**
> Each brand of data logging equipment will have a different set-up procedure.

> **Tip**
> Your data logger may calculate the speeds for you, or otherwise you can use the equation:
> $$\text{speed} = \frac{\text{length of interrupt card}}{\text{time taken}}$$

> **Tip**
> You may want to tape the additional masses down if there is nothing to attach them to.

Observations

Part A

Mass on mass hanger / kg	Force applied (weight) / N	Initial speed / m/s	Distance between final two dots / m	Final speed / m/s	Number of dots between start and end of journey	Time for journey / s	Acceleration / m/s²

> **Tip**
> The equations needed to complete this table are provided in the
> **Key equations** box on pages 146 and 147.

Part B

Length of black card = ...

Mass of trolley / kg	Time passing light gate 1 / s	Initial velocity / m/s	Time passing light gate 2 / s	Final velocity / m/s	Total time / s	Acceleration / m/s²

Conclusions

Part A

1 Describe the spacing of the ticker tape dots between the start and the end of the trolley's journey. Suggest what this tells you about the motion of the trolley.

....

....

2 Describe the ticker tape patterns that are produced as you add more weight to the pulley. Suggest what this implies about the relationship between force and acceleration.

....

....

....

Part B

3 Describe what happens to the acceleration of the trolley as you increase its mass.

....

....

4 Are mass and acceleration directly proportional or indirectly proportional?

....

....

Evaluation

5 In a perfect world, you would expect that doubling the force applied to the trolley would double its acceleration. Suggest why your results might **not** follow this relationship.

....

....

....

....

6 State the advantages of using light gates and a data logger over other methods of measuring acceleration, such as ticker tape.

....

....

....

....

Physics

Exam-style questions

1 This diagram shows the horizontal forces acting on a car.

1000 N   640 N

a) Which one of these statements describes the motion of the car? **[1]**
   - slowing down
   - stationary
   - at a constant speed
   - speeding up

b) During a part of the journey, the car accelerates from 5 m/s to 15 m/s in 5 s.
   Calculate the acceleration of the car. **[2]**

   ....

   ....

   acceleration = ... m/s^2

c) Calculate the resultant force acting on the car while accelerating.
   The mass of the car is 1200 kg. Include an appropriate unit. **[3]**

   ....

   ....

   resultant force = ... (unit: ....)

d) Calculate the distance travelled while the car is accelerating. **[3]**
   final velocity^2 − initial velocity^2 = 2 × acceleration × distance

   ....

   ....

   ....

   distance = ... m

2 The velocity–time graph below shows how the velocity of a skydiver changes as she falls.

   Describe her motion at points A–E, referring to the forces acting on her. **[6]**

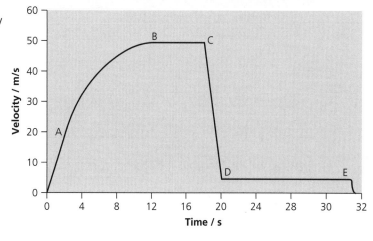

....

....

....

....

....

....

[Total = ... / 15 marks]

Further application

Key term 🔑

Recoil: the backwards movement of a gun when it is fired.

1 A bullet of mass 0.02 kg is fired from a gun. The shooter feels a force of 20 N due to the **recoil**.

a) State the force on the bullet. [1]

....

....

b) Calculate the acceleration of the bullet. [2]

c) The bullet is accelerated down a barrel of length 50 cm. What velocity will the bullet have as it leaves the barrel? [3]

Key equation x+y=z

final velocity² – initial velocity² = 2 × acceleration × distance

d) The time it takes a bullet to hit the ground when fired horizontally is the same as if it was dropped vertically from rest. [4]

Show that it takes about 0.6 s to fall 2 m.

Tip 💡

The acceleration due to gravity is 9.8 m/s².

e) How far will the fired bullet travel horizontally? [2]

[Total = ... / 12 marks]

Physics

Required practical 20: Investigating the frequency, wavelength and speed of waves in solids and liquids

A wave is a repetitive vibration that transfers energy but not matter. Although the particles transmitting the wave move up and down or side-to-side, they return to their original position once they have passed the energy on. Waves are essential to modern life as all information is transferred by waves in some form. Without waves, we would have no communication.

The three main wave properties of a wave that can be measured are **wave speed**, **frequency** and **wavelength**. They are linked by the wave equation:

$v = f\lambda$

where

- v is wave speed
- f is frequency
- λ is wavelength

Aim

Make observations to identify the suitability of apparatus to measure the frequency, wavelength and speed of waves both in a ripple tank, as well as waves in a solid, and take appropriate measurements.

Note

It is likely that these practicals will be conducted as a teacher demonstration as your school may not have enough equipment for everybody to use. Alternatively, a simulation of the experiment can be found at https://phet.colorado.edu

Equipment

- Pulley
- String or elastic cord
- Slotted 100 g masses
- 100 g mass hanger
- Signal generator
- Vibration generator
- Wooden bridge
- Metre rule
- Ripple tank
- Vibration generator
- Variable power supply
- Digital camera or mobile phone with camera and video capability
- Timer
- White paper
- Water

Further information can be found in **AQA GCSE (9–1) Combined Science Student Book** on these pages:
- 611–612: Waves in air, fluids and solids (*or CS 2: 255–256*)
- 613–614: Properties of waves (*or CS 2: 257–258*)
- 615–617: Measuring wave speeds (*or CS 2: 259–261*).

Key terms

Wave speed: how quickly a wave travels through the medium (or material) it is travelling through, measured in metres per second, m/s.

Frequency: the number of times a wave passes a point per second, measured in hertz, Hz.

Wavelength: the distance between two identical points on neighbouring waves (such as from peak to peak), measured in metres, m.

Health and safety

- Wear eye protection when you are near the vibrating string.
- Take care with masses over the pulley – make sure your feet are not underneath in case they fall.
- Be careful when using electrical equipment near water. Be sure to wipe up any water spills as soon as possible to prevent slips and falls.
- Put a padded box beneath the masses to prevent damage to the masses and the floor when they fall.

Maths opportunities

- Substituting numerical values into algebraic equations using appropriate units for physical quantities
- Changing the subject of an equation
- Understanding that $y = mx + c$ represents a linear relationship
- Plotting two variables from experimental or other data
- Determining the slope of a linear graph

Key equation

$v = f\lambda$

Method

Part A: Measuring waves through a solid

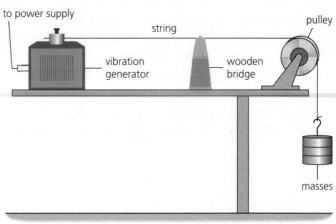

1 Set up the equipment as shown in the diagram.
   a) Clamp the pulley to the edge of the bench.
   b) Attach the vibration generator to the signal generator on the other end of the bench, just over 1 m away from the pulley.
   c) Tie a piece of string or elastic cord (about 1.5 m long) to the vibration generator. Tie the other end to a 100 g mass hanger. Hang the mass hanger over the pulley.
   d) Place the wooden bridge 1 m away from the vibration generator.
2 Set the signal generator to a low frequency. Turn on the vibration generator. The string will start to vibrate but not in an obvious wave shape.
3 Slowly increase the frequency of the signal generator until you get a full, single wave pattern. Make sure you have exactly two peaks and troughs, like this:

4 Complete the first row of the results table in the **observations** section by:
   • reading the frequency off the signal generator
   • measuring the wavelength (the distance between the vibration generator and the bridge)
   • calculating wave speed using the wave equation.
5 Vary the distance between the bridge and the vibration generator. Repeat steps 2–4 two more times to complete the results table.

Part B: Measuring waves through a liquid

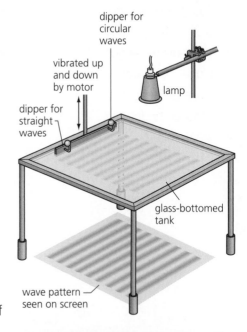

1 Set up the equipment as shown in the diagram.
   a) Place the ripple tank on a table or other surface over a piece of white paper.
   b) Fill the ripple tank with water to a depth of about 0.5 cm.
   c) Place the dipper into the water, at the very edge of the ripple tank.
   d) Attach the dipper to the power supply.
2 Turn on the power supply. Set it to a low voltage. Gradually increase the voltage until you get a clear pattern of waves in the ripple tank.
3 Take a photograph of the ripple tank, with a ruler alongside, so you can measure the distance between adjacent peaks. This is the wavelength. Record this value in the results table in the **observations** section.
4 Record a video of the ripple tank for 10 seconds, with a stopwatch in shot. Watch the video back in slow motion and count how many waves pass a point in 10 seconds. Dividing this number by 10 will tell you the frequency of the wave. Record it in the results table.
5 Calculate the wave speed using the wave equation. Record it in the results table.
6 Vary the voltage on the power supply so that the waves are produced at a different rate. Repeat steps 3–5 and calculate the wavelength, frequency and wave speed again.

> **Note**
>
> Different ripple tanks have different set ups, so you may have to vary this method slightly depending on the equipment you have available.

Physics

Observations

Part A

Frequency / Hz	Wavelength / m	Wave speed / m/s

Part B

Frequency / Hz	Wavelength / m	Wave speed / m/s

Conclusions

1   For both experiments, identify the relationship between wavelength and frequency.

....

....

....

> **Tip**
> Think about what happens to wavelength as you increase frequency, and vice versa.

Evaluation

2   Give one possible systematic error associated with Part A.

....

3   When conducting Part B, which measurement had the highest amount of uncertainty?

....

4   Why was this the case in Part B?

....

....

5   Describe how to improve the accuracy of the measurement you have identified. Consider the equipment used for this experiment as part of your answer.

....

....

....

Exam-style questions

1   A student sits on a harbour wall watching the waves hit. Over the course of one minute, 20 waves hit the harbour wall.

The student estimates that the distance between two wave crests is 6 m.

Assuming their estimation is correct, how fast are the waves travelling?   **[3]**

....

....

....

....

2   A student hits an iron girder of length 0.8 m with a hammer. The time period of the vibration through the metal is 0.31 ms. The wavelength of the vibration is 1.6 m.

a)   What is the frequency of the wave? Give an appropriate unit.   **[3]**

....

....

....

....

b)   The student says that the speed of the vibration through the iron girder is approximately 5200 m/s. Determine whether the student is correct.   **[2]**

....

....

....

....

c)   Calculate how long it would take for the vibration to reach the other end of the girder.   **[3]**

....

....

....

....

Physics

HT **3** Fishermen often use ultrasound to find shoals of fish underneath their boats.

The graph shows a pulse sent out by the boat and two reflected pulses received. The reflected pulse, R_1, is caused by a shoal of fish. R_2 is caused by the ocean floor.

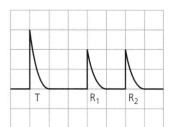

a) Each division on the horizontal axis represents 20 ms.

Calculate the time it takes between the transmitted pulse, T, and the first reflected pulse, R_1. **[1]**

....

....

b) The speed of ultrasound in water is 1500 m/s.

How far below the boat is the shoal of fish? **[3]**

....

....

....

....

c) The reflected wave R_2 is due to the ocean floor.

Calculate the depth of the ocean below the boat. **[4]**

....

....

....

....

[Total = ... / 19 marks]

Further application

1 A student tuned a guitar. They noticed that, as the tension force stretching the guitar string increased, the frequency of the note made by the string increased.

The student decided to investigate the relationship between the tension force stretching one of the strings and the frequency of the note produced by the string.

The length of a guitar string is 0.65 m.

a) What is the independent variable? [1]

....

....

b) What is the dependent variable? [1]

....

....

c) Give **two** control variables. [2]

....

....

d) Suggest one risk that this investigation might cause. Describe what safety precaution the student should take. [2]

....

....

A teacher told the student they could calculate the tension of the guitar string using this equation

$$f = \frac{1}{2l}\sqrt{\frac{T}{\mu}}$$

where
f is frequency, in Hz
l is length of the guitar string, in m
T is tension force of the string, in N
μ is the mass per unit length of the guitar string, in kg/m

(HT) e) Re-arrange the equation to make T the subject of the formula. [3]

> **Tip**
> Start by finding the equation for f^2.

(HT) f) Show that the value of tension of the string is around 50 N.

The mass of one metre of the guitar string is 2.35 g.

> **Tip**
> You may need to use a calculator.

The frequency of the note is 110 Hz. [2]

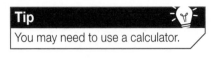

Physics

The student then investigated another string on the guitar which had an unknown value of μ.

As they increased the tension force, they measured the frequency of note produced.

The length of this string was identical to the previous string.

Frequency / Hz	Tension / N	Frequency^2 / Hz^2
66	30	
71	34	
75	38	
79	42	
84	48	
87	52	

g) Complete the table. Plot a graph of *tension* (*y*-axis) against *frequency*^{2} (*x*-axis). **[9]**

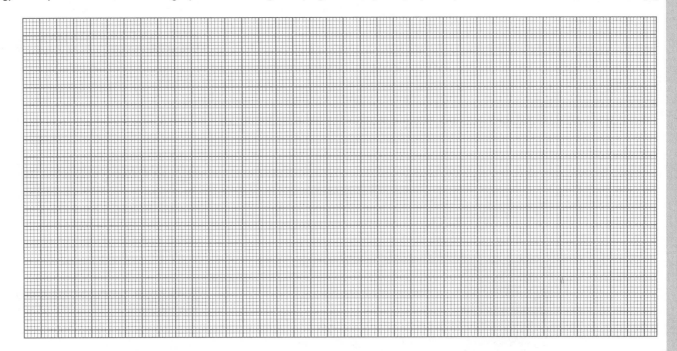

h) Draw a line of best fit and calculate the gradient, *G*. **[3]**

i) Using your gradient *G*, find μ, the mass of one metre of the wire.

$G = 4l^2\mu$ **[3]**

[Total = ... / 26 marks]

Required practical 21: Investigating how much infrared radiation is absorbed or radiated by a surface

Infrared radiation is a type of electromagnetic radiation, commonly known as heat. Any object that has thermal energy will emit infrared radiation. The amount of infrared radiation that an object emits depends on its temperature and the properties of its surface.

> ### Key terms
>
> **Infrared radiation:** a form of electromagnetic radiation; partially responsible for the transfer of thermal energy.
>
> **Leslie cube:** a metal box with different coloured surfaces on each side, usually matt black, shiny black, metallic (such as silver or copper), matt white and shiny white.

Aim

Investigate how the amount of infrared radiation absorbed or radiated by a surface depends on the nature of that surface.

Equipment

- **Leslie cube**
- Kettle
- Heatproof mat
- Funnel
- Digital thermometer
- Ruler

Method

1 Place the Leslie cube onto the heatproof mat.

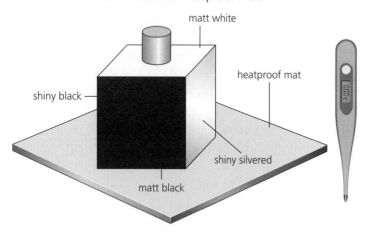

matt white

heatproof mat

shiny black

shiny silvered

matt black

2 Boil some water in the kettle. Pour it into the Leslie cube.
3 Use the digital thermometer to take a temperature reading for each surface. You may need to wait a few moments for your thermometer to stabilise. Record these values in the results table in the **observations** section.
4 Wait for the Leslie cube to cool. Pour out the water. Put the equipment away.

Further information can be found in **AQA GCSE (9–1) Combined Science Student Book** on these pages:

- 622–625: Uses and applications of electromagnetic waves (*or CS 2: 266–269*).

> ### Health and safety
>
> - Take care when using hot or boiling water.
> - The Leslie cube should be placed on a heatproof mat before being filled and then not touched until it has cooled down.
> - Use a funnel to fill the Leslie cube.

> ### Maths opportunities
>
> - Translating information between graphical and numeric form
> - Plotting two variables from experimental or other data
> - Changing the subject of an equation

> ### Note
>
> This practical may be presented as a teacher demonstration or in large groups as it is unlikely there will be enough Leslie cubes available for students to work individually.

> ### Tip
>
> Use a ruler so that you take all temperature readings from the same distance from each side.

Physics

Observations

Description of side	Temperature / °C

Conclusions

1 a) State which material was

i)   the best emitter of infrared radiation

....

ii) the worst emitter of infrared radiation.

....

b) Give reasons for your answers.

....

....

....

Evaluation

2   This experiment is notorious for giving inaccurate results. Suggest a way to improve the method.

....

....

....

Exam-style questions

1   A school's radiators are painted with white gloss paint. Give **two** ways someone could improve these radiators to heat the school more efficiently.   **[2]**

....

....

....

....

2   A student poured boiling water into a Leslie cube. They took temperature readings of each side of the Leslie cube every 10 minutes. This table shows their results.

Colour of side	Time / mins							
	0	10	20	30	40	50	60	70
	Temperature / °C							
Black	80	65	52	43	35	30	25	20
Copper	70	57	45	38	31	27	24	20
White	65	50	40	33	28	25	23	20
Silver	55	40	33	28	25	23	21	20

a)   Plot these results on a graph. Add a line of best fit for each side.   **[4]**

b)   Use the graph to determine the temperature reading on the copper side of the cube after 15 minutes.   **[1]**

....

....

c) Explain why you would expect the temperature of each side to show no further reduction in temperature after 70 minutes. [1]

....

....

3 An engineer at a saucepan manufacturer is looking into improving the design of their range. They want to see if painting grey pans will reduce the time it takes water to boil.

The engineer chose four different paints to test: white gloss, shiny silver, grey (no paint) and matt black.

a) Give **two** control variables. [2]

....

....

....

....

b) Suggest **one** risk that this investigation might cause. Describe what safety precaution the engineer should take. [2]

....

....

....

....

This table shows the results of the engineer's test.

Colour of paint	White gloss	Shiny silver	Grey (no paint)	Matt black
Time taken for water to boil / mins	3.5	3.7	3.0	2.8

c) Calculate how much longer it took for water to boil in the saucepan painted with white gloss paint, compared to the saucepan painted in matt black paint. Give your answer in seconds. [2]

....

....

....

....

d) Matt black was the best paint to use. Suggest why the manufacturers may be reluctant to change their design. [2]

....

....

....

....

[Total = ... / 16 marks]

Further application

1   A student wanted to find out the power output of the Sun.

They used a beaker containing 300 g of cola and a thermometer. They left the cola outside when the Sun was directly overhead to absorb the thermal energy from the Sun.

The student took an initial temperature measurement of 20.2 °C, waited 10 minutes, and then took a final temperature measurement of 22.1 °C.

thermometer

beaker

cola

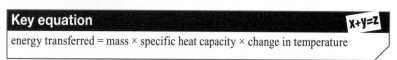

Key equation   **x+y=z**

energy transferred = mass × specific heat capacity × change in temperature

a) Calculate the energy transferred to the cola.

Assume the specific heat capacity of cola is 4200 J/kg °C.   **[2]**

b) Calculate the joules of energy absorbed by the cola per second.   **[2]**

c) The sunlight falls onto the circular surface of the cola of radius 5.0 cm. Using your answer to part b), calculate the power of the Sun per square metre hitting the surface of the cola.   **[2]**

Physics

d) The distance from the Earth to the Sun is approximately 1.5×10^{11} m.

At this distance, the energy given off by the Sun covers the surface area of a sphere of radius 1.5×10^{11} m.

Using the equation below, calculate this surface area. **[2]**

surface area of a sphere $= 4\pi r^2$

e) Using your answers to parts b) and c), calculate the total power output of the Sun. **[2]**

f) State the amount of energy the Sun emits per second. **[1]**

....

....

g) Scientists have calculated the actual power output of the Sun to be 3.8×10^{26} W.
Give **two** reasons why your value was much lower. **[2]**

....

....

....

....

h) Why did the student use cola and not water? **[1]**

....

....

....

[Total = ... / 14 marks]

Biology key equations

Topic	Word equation
Total magnification	total magnification = magnification of eyepieces lens $\times$ magnification of the objective lens
Real size	$\text{real size} = \dfrac{\text{image size}}{\text{magnification}}$
Magnification of a drawing	$\text{magnification} = \dfrac{\text{length of drawing of cell}}{\text{actual length of cell}}$
Photosynthesis	carbon dioxide + water $\xrightarrow{\text{light}}$ glucose + oxygen
Mean average	$\text{mean} = \dfrac{\text{sum of results}}{\text{total number results}}$
Estimated population size	$\text{estimated population size} = \dfrac{\text{total area}}{\text{area sampled}} \times \text{number of plants counted}$

Chemistry key equations

Topic	Word equation	Symbol equation
Mean averages	$$\text{mean} = \frac{\text{sum of results}}{\text{total number of results}}$$	
Percentages	$$\text{percentage yield} = \frac{\text{(actual yield} \times 100\%)}{\text{predicted yield}}$$	
Relative formula mass	relative formula mass (M_r) = the relative atomic mass for all the atoms in a substance's chemical formula	
(HT) Molar mass	The molar mass of a substance is its relative formula mass (M_r) in grams (g/mol)	
(HT) Moles	$$\text{amount of substance} = \frac{\text{mass of substance}}{\text{relative formula mass}}$$	$$g = \frac{mol}{g/mol}$$
(HT) Moles	$$\frac{\text{mass}}{\text{moles} \times \text{molar mass}}$$	$$\frac{g}{mol \times g/mol}$$
Reaction rate (relating to colour change or change in turbidity)	rate = 1 ÷ reaction time	
Reaction rate	$$\text{reaction rate} = \frac{\text{amount of reactant OR amount of product formed}}{\text{time taken}}$$ This is adjusted for specific reactions. For example: $$\text{reaction rate (cm}^3\text{/s)} = \frac{\text{volume of gas (cm}^3\text{)}}{\text{time taken (s)}}$$	
Energy changes	heat energy transferred (in joules, J) = mass of the liquid (in grams, g) × specific heat capacity of the liquid (in J/g°C) × temperature rise (in degrees Celsius, °C) The specific heat capacity of water is 4.2 J/g°C, but this value is also used for other liquids (e.g. acids).	$Q = mc\,\Delta T$
Graph gradients	The equation of a straight line on a graph consists of a y term, an x term and a number. It is written as $y = mx + c$. The value of m represents the gradient of the line and can be calculated by dividing the change in y by the change in x: $$\text{gradient} = \frac{\text{change in } y}{\text{change in } x}$$ c is the y-intercept and can be found by finding where the straight line meets the y-axis.	$y = mx + c$
Chromatography	$$R_f = \frac{\text{distance travelled by component}}{\text{distance travelled by solvent}}$$ R_f value is the ratio of the distance moved by a substance to the distance moved by the solvent during chromatography.	

Physics key equations

Topic	Word equation	Symbol equation
Energy	kinetic energy = 0.5 × mass × speed^2	$E_k = \dfrac{1}{2} m v^2$
Energy	gravitational potential energy = mass × gravitational field strength (g) × height	$E_p = m g h$
Energy	elastic potential energy = 0.5 × spring constant × (extension)^2	$E_e = \dfrac{1}{2} k e^2$
Energy	change in thermal energy = mass × specific heat capacity × temperature change	$\Delta E = m c \Delta \theta$
Energy	$E = mc\Delta\theta$	
Energy	power = $\dfrac{\text{energy transferred}}{\text{time}}$	$P = \dfrac{E}{t}$
Energy	power = $\dfrac{\text{work done}}{\text{time}}$	$P = \dfrac{W}{t}$
Energy	efficiency = $\dfrac{\text{useful output energy transfer}}{\text{total input energy transfer}}$	
Energy	efficiency = $\dfrac{\text{useful power output}}{\text{total power input}}$	
Electricity	charge flow = current × time	$Q = I t$
Electricity	potential difference = current × resistance	$V = I R$
Electricity	power = potential difference × current	$P = V I$
Electricity	power = (current)^2 × resistance	$P = I^2 R$
Electricity	energy transferred = power × time	$E = P t$
Electricity	energy transferred = charge flow × potential difference	$E = Q V$
Particle model of matter	density = $\dfrac{\text{mass}}{\text{volume}}$ This can be applied to different situations. For example: density of saltwater = $\dfrac{\text{mass of water} + \text{mass of salt}}{\text{volume of saltwater}}$	$\rho = \dfrac{m}{V}$
Particle model of matter	thermal energy for a change of state = mass × specific latent heat	$E = m L$
Particle model of matter	For gases: pressure × volume = constant	$p V = \text{constant}$
Forces	weight = mass × gravitational field strength (g)	$W = m g$
Forces	work done = force × distance along the line of action of the force	$W = F s$
Forces	force applied to a spring = spring constant × extension	$F = k e$
Forces	moment of a force = force × distance (normal to direction of force)	$M = F d$
Forces	pressure = $\dfrac{\text{force normal to a surface}}{\text{area of that surface}}$	$p = \dfrac{F}{A}$
(HT) Forces	pressure due to a column of liquid = height of column × density of liquid × gravitational field strength	$p = h \rho g$

Topic	Word equation	Symbol equation
Forces	distance travelled = speed × time	$s = v\,t$
Forces	acceleration = $\dfrac{\text{change in velocity}}{\text{time taken}}$	$a = \dfrac{\Delta v}{t}$
Forces	(final velocity)^2 – (initial velocity)^2 = 2 × acceleration × distance	$v^2 - u^2 = 2\,a\,s$
Forces	resultant force = mass × acceleration	$F = m\,a$
(HT) Forces	momentum = mass × velocity	$p = m\,v$
(HT) Forces	force = $\dfrac{\text{change in momentum}}{\text{time taken}}$	$F = \dfrac{m\,\Delta v}{\Delta t}$
Forces	gradient = $\dfrac{\text{change in } y}{\text{change in } x}$	
Waves	wave speed = frequency × wavelength	$v = f\,\lambda$
Waves	period = $\dfrac{1}{\text{frequency}}$	
Waves	magnification = $\dfrac{\text{image height}}{\text{object height}}$	
Magnetism and electromagnetism	Ohm's law is resistance = $\dfrac{\text{voltage}}{\text{current}}$ Alternatively, resistance (Ω) = $\dfrac{\text{potential difference (V)}}{\text{current (A)}}$	$R = \dfrac{V}{I}$
Magnetism and electromagnetism	resistance = $\dfrac{\text{resistivity} \times \text{length}}{\text{cross sectional area}}$	
(HT) Magnetism and electromagnetism	$\dfrac{\text{potential difference across primary coil}}{\text{potential difference across secondary coil}} = \dfrac{\text{number of turns in primary coil}}{\text{number of turns in secondary coil}}$	$\dfrac{V_\text{p}}{V_\text{s}} = \dfrac{n_\text{p}}{n_\text{s}}$
(HT) Magnetism and electromagnetism	$\dfrac{\text{potential difference}}{\text{across primary coil}} \times \dfrac{\text{current in}}{\text{primary coil}} = \dfrac{\text{potential difference}}{\text{across secondary coil}} \times \dfrac{\text{current in}}{\text{secondary coil}}$	$V_\text{p} \times I_\text{p} = V_\text{s} \times I_\text{s}$
(HT) Magnetism and electromagnetism	$\dfrac{\text{force on a conductor (at right angles}}{\text{to a magnetic field) carrying a current}} = \dfrac{\text{magnetic flux}}{\text{density}} \times \text{current} \times \text{length}$	$F = B\,I\,l$
General	area of a circle = πr^2	$A = \pi r^2$
General	surface area to volume ratio = $\dfrac{\text{surface area}}{\text{volume}}$	
General	volume = length × width × height	
General	extension, e = extended length – original length	
General	angle of incidence = angle of reflection	

Biology key terms

Carbohydrate: a group of organic compounds that includes sugars, starch and cellulose. They contain carbon, hydrogen and oxygen.

Cell sap: the solution found in the central vacuole of plant cells. Sugars are the principal solutes.

Enzyme: a biological catalyst, which speeds up the rate of a given reaction without taking part in it.

Epidermis: the outer layer of cells covering an organism.

Graticule: a glass disc with a measurement scale engraved on it, inserted into the eyepiece of a microscope.

Light intensity: the brightness of a light.

Lipids: a group of organic compounds that are oily to the touch and insoluble in water. Lipids include fatty acids, oils, waxes and triglycerides (fats).

Osmosis: the net movement of water molecules through a selectively permeable membrane from a more dilute solution to a more concentrated solution.

pH: a measure of the acidity or alkalinity of a solution.

Photosynthesis: the process by which green plants make food, using carbon dioxide, water and light energy.

Proteins: a group of organic compounds that are large molecules composed of one or more long chains of amino acids.

Quadrat: a frame of a specified area.

Qualitative test: a test that indicates the presence or absence of a substance, but gives no information about its quantity.

Random sampling: samples that are taken randomly to avoid human influence or bias.

Transect: a surveying technique that samples at points distributed along a line or a narrow band.

Water potential: a measure of the tendency of water to move from one area to another due to osmosis.

Chemistry key terms

Aqueous: similar to water or dissolved in water.

Binary ionic compound: a compound made up of ions of two different elements – one metal and one non-metal.

Compound: a substance made from two or more different elements chemically joined together.

Desalination: removal of dissolved solids from seawater.

Distillation: the separation of a specific liquid (usually the solvent) from a solution.

Electrolysis: the decomposition of ionic compounds using electricity.

Electrolyte: an ionic liquid or solution of aqueous ions that conducts electricity during electrolysis.

Electroplating: forming a layer of another metal onto a metal object using electrolysis.

Endothermic reaction: a reaction that absorbs heat energy (and so causes a decrease in temperature).

Exothermic reaction: a reaction that releases heat energy (and so causes an increase in temperature).

Hypothesis: a prediction or proposed explanation based on probable evidence.

Mobile phase: the liquid or gas that flows through a chromatography system, moving the materials to be separated over the stationary phase.

Neutralisation: the reaction between an acid and an alkali, base, carbonate or metal that produces a salt with a pH of 7.

Potable water: water that is safe to drink.

Purification: the separation of a mixture into separate elements or compounds.

R_f value: the ratio of the distance moved by a substance to the distance moved by the solvent during chromatography.

Solute: a gas or solid that is dissolved in a solvent, such as water, to form a solution.

Solvent: a liquid that dissolves a solid or gas to form a solution.

Stationary phase: the solid or liquid phase of a chromatography system which causes the materials to be separated to move at different rates.

Turbidity: the cloudiness of a solution.

Physics key terms

Acceleration: the rate of change of velocity.

Coulomb: the measurement unit for charge; each electron has a tiny charge of -1.6×10^{-19} C.

Cross sectional area: the two-dimensional area you would see when you cut into a wire.

Current: a flow of electrical charge; the size of the electric current is the rate of flow of electrical charge; it is measured in amperes (A).

Data logger: an electronic device that uses sensors to record data over time; data loggers can often take readings more frequently and to a higher resolution than other measuring devices, so they are more accurate and, therefore, better for practical work.

Displacement technique: used to find the volume of an object by measuring the volume of water displaced (pushed up or removed) by the object.

Extension: the difference between the stretched and unstretched lengths of a spring.

Frequency: the number of times a wave passes a point per second, measured in hertz, Hz.

Infrared radiation: a form of electromagnetic radiation; partially responsible for the transfer of thermal energy.

Leslie cube: a metal box with different coloured surfaces on each side, usually matt black, shiny black, metallic (such as silver or copper), matt white and shiny white.

Ohm's law: the current flowing through a resistor at a constant temperature is directly proportional to the voltage across the resistor.

Parallax error: when looking at an object you are using to measure a value, it can appear in a different position than its actual position because of your line of sight.

Parallel: in a parallel circuit, two or more components are connected to the same points in the circuit.

Potential difference (p.d.): a measure of the work done, or energy transferred to a component, by each coulomb of charge that passes through it; it is measured in volts (V).

Potential dividers: 'split up' the voltage within a circuit, so that parts of a circuit only get the voltage they need; they are usually made up of two or more resistors arranged in series across a power supply.

Recoil: the backwards movement of a gun when it is fired.

Resolution: the smallest possible quantity being measured by a measuring instrument that will show a noticeable change in the reading.

Series: in a series circuit, components are connected one after another in a complete circuit loop.

Springs in parallel: when springs are added side by side.

Springs in series: when springs are added end to end.

Thermal equilibrium: two substances in thermal equilibrium are at the same temperature.

Velocity: an object's speed in a given direction.

Wave speed: how quickly a wave travels through the medium (or material) it is travelling through, measured in metres per second, m/s.

Wavelength: the distance between two identical points on neighbouring waves (such as from peak to peak), measured in metres, m.

Notes and calculations